Skills Techniques and Decision Making

St. Ciarans's College
15 Tullybrynn Road
Ballygawley, Co. Tyrone
BT70 2LY
Tel No: 028 855 68640

Skills Techniques and Decision Making

FOR A LEVEL GEOGRAPHY

COLOURPOINT
EDUCATIONAL

Rewarding Learning

Stephen Roulston
Mary Reid

© Roulston, Reid and Colourpoint Books, 2004, 2008

ISBN: 978 1 904242 97 0

Second Edition
Third Impression

Layout and design: Colourpoint Books
Printed by: GPS Colour Graphics Ltd, Belfast

**COLOURPOINT
EDUCATIONAL**

Colourpoint Educational
An imprint of Colourpoint Creative Ltd
Colourpoint House
Jubilee Business Park
21 Jubilee Road
Newtownards
County Down
Northern Ireland
BT23 4YH

Tel: 028 9182 6339
Fax: 028 9182 1900
E-mail: info@colourpoint.co.uk
Web site: www.colourpoint.co.uk

Mary Reid, BSc (Hons), PGCE, is head of Geography in Dominican College, Belfast. She graduated from QUB and taught Geography in St Louise's Comprehensive College before her appointment to Dominican College in 1993. She has wide experience working with a number of examining boards but is currently a Principal Examiner for AS Geography with CCEA.

With gratitude and thanks to Tony, Catherine, Ellen and Thomas.

Stephen Roulston, BEd, MA, DPhil, taught Geography briefly at Foyle and Londonderry College, and then moved to Ballymena Academy, becoming Head of the Geography Department there. He now works with C2k as an e-Learning Consultant. He has been Principal Examiner for A2 Geography with CCEA for some years.

To Irwin and Maureen, for all their help

Contents

Section 1	**AS Fieldwork Report**	4
1.1	The AS Fieldwork Report – What should be included?	8
1.2	The table of data	9
Section 2	**Data Collection**	13
2.1	Sampling	13
2.2	Vegetation Sampling	18
2.3	Questionnaires	21
Section 3	**Statistical Methods**	24
3.1	Measures of Central Tendency	24
3.2	Measures of Dispersion	27
3.3	Correlation	28
3.4	Nearest Neighbour Analysis	35
3.5	Chi-squared Statistic ⭐A2	41
3.6	Location Quotient ⭐A2	47
Section 4	**Graphical Presentation and Mapping Techniques**	50
4.1	Barcharts	50
4.2	Line Graphs	53
4.3	Pie Charts	54
4.4	Proportional Graphs	56
4.5	Triangular Graphs	58
4.6	Scatter Graphs	61
4.7	Choropleth Maps	64
4.8	Dot Distribution Maps	66
4.9	Flow Line Maps	67
4.10	Annotated Sketch Maps	68
4.11	Isoline Maps	70
Section 5	**Decision Making** ⭐A2	72
5.1	Written resources	72
5.2	Structure	76
5.3	Techniques	79

The ⭐A2 symbol indicates content relevant only to those studying the subject at A2 level

1 AS Fieldwork Report

Fieldwork is an essential component of the AS and A2 geography specification. If the study is well planned, focusing on a precise aim and conducted in an organised manner, with thorough follow-up, then geography fieldwork can become an exciting learning experience. It can enhance knowledge and understanding of the environment and help develop a more confident and competent approach to geographical studies.

In the AS1 examination a **fieldwork report** must be prepared and submitted along with a **table of data** collected in the field. The essential requirements for this table and report will be examined in detail but it is necessary for pupils and teachers to realise that they form an integral component of the fieldwork process. All stages of the geographical investigation **process** need to be followed through rigorously and reflectively in the classroom. This should allow maximum marks to be gained in Question 1 of the AS1 examination paper, which relates to all aspects of the fieldwork. The stages are outlined in Figure 1.

Figure 1 Schematic diagram illustrating the geographical investigation process

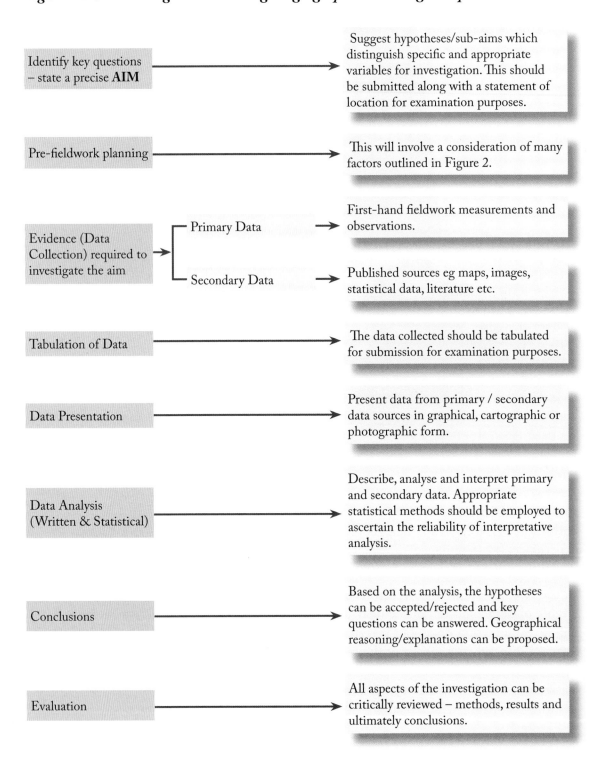

Identify key questions – state a precise **AIM**	Suggest hypotheses/sub-aims which distinguish specific and appropriate variables for investigation. This should be submitted along with a statement of location for examination purposes.
Pre-fieldwork planning	This will involve a consideration of many factors outlined in Figure 2.
Evidence (Data Collection) required to investigate the aim — Primary Data	First-hand fieldwork measurements and observations.
— Secondary Data	Published sources eg maps, images, statistical data, literature etc.
Tabulation of Data	The data collected should be tabulated for submission for examination purposes.
Data Presentation	Present data from primary / secondary data sources in graphical, cartographic or photographic form.
Data Analysis (Written & Statistical)	Describe, analyse and interpret primary and secondary data. Appropriate statistical methods should be employed to ascertain the reliability of interpretative analysis.
Conclusions	Based on the analysis, the hypotheses can be accepted/rejected and key questions can be answered. Geographical reasoning/explanations can be proposed.
Evaluation	All aspects of the investigation can be critically reviewed – methods, results and ultimately conclusions.

Figure 2 : Fieldwork planning

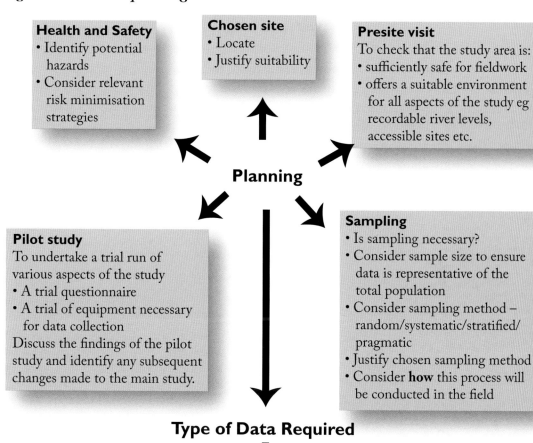

Health and Safety
- Identify potential hazards
- Consider relevant risk minimisation strategies

Chosen site
- Locate
- Justify suitability

Presite visit
To check that the study area is:
- sufficiently safe for fieldwork
- offers a suitable environment for all aspects of the study eg recordable river levels, accessible sites etc.

Planning

Pilot study
To undertake a trial run of various aspects of the study
- A trial questionnaire
- A trial of equipment necessary for data collection
Discuss the findings of the pilot study and identify any subsequent changes made to the main study.

Sampling
- Is sampling necessary?
- Consider sample size to ensure data is representative of the total population
- Consider sampling method – random/systematic/stratified/pragmatic
- Justify chosen sampling method
- Consider **how** this process will be conducted in the field

Type of Data Required

Primary data
- Consider the **type** of data necessary to explore the aim, or test the hypotheses devised.
- Consider the **volume** of data required for valid statistical analysis.
- Design data recording sheets/questionnaires.

Secondary data
- Select published sources of data which may be of relevance to the study.
- Consider **how** and **where** these sources may be obtained.

1.1 The AS Fieldwork Report –
What should be included?

As outlined in the Revised Geography Specification, there is a requirement for candidates to submit a succinct fieldwork report and a table of data in advance of the AS1 examination. These materials may be centre produced and marks are not awarded for their inclusion. However, submission is vital for the attainment of marks in Section A of AS1. The summary statement submitted provides the spatial and theoretical context of the study allowing examiners to verify candidates' responses regarding fieldwork knowledge. The table of data is essential to enable candidates to present, analyse, statistically test and interpret their findings in an examination setting.

The Fieldwork Report

A concise report of approximately 100 words should outline:

- A specific title for the fieldwork.

- A brief statement of the aims/ purpose/issues which provide the theoretical context for the personal investigation element of the fieldwork. The general aim may be developed into key questions/hypotheses.

- A brief outline of the location, the spatial context of the study, may be illustrated on a location map.

Take Note

Candidates **should not** address any other aspects of the investigation in this summary statement. Questions in Section A of the AS1 examination will require the candidate to draw on their knowledge, skills and experiences gained throughout all stages of the investigation process.

The Fieldwork must arise from, or be linked closely to, the theoretical concepts outlined in the AS1 or AS2 units of study.

The use of ICT is desirable for the presentation of the report.

1.2 The Table of Data

The data collected in the field should be tabulated and submitted as part of the AS1 exam paper. There are a number of essential requirements.

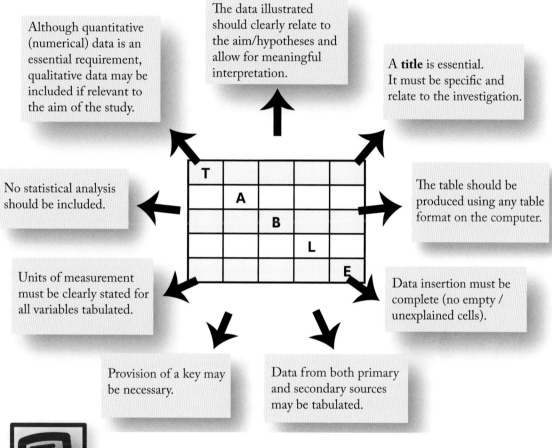

Although quantitative (numerical) data is an essential requirement, qualitative data may be included if relevant to the aim of the study.

The data illustrated should clearly relate to the aim/hypotheses and allow for meaningful interpretation.

A **title** is essential. It must be specific and relate to the investigation.

No statistical analysis should be included.

The table should be produced using any table format on the computer.

Units of measurement must be clearly stated for all variables tabulated.

Data insertion must be complete (no empty / unexplained cells).

Provision of a key may be necessary.

Data from both primary and secondary sources may be tabulated.

Exam Tip

This table should be studied closely before the examination as its use will be required for parts of Section A on the AS1 exam paper.

You **may** be asked to:

- present the data using an appropriate **graphical technique** (refer to Section 4)
- analyse the data using an appropriate **statistical technique** (refer to Section 3)

Figure 3 Student Checklist

Report	YES	NO
Have I provided a specific title for my fieldwork report?	☐	☐
Have I presented a precise statement of the Aim, with possible sub-aims/hypotheses, to provide clarification on the purpose of the study?	☐	☐
Have I included a statement of location for the investigation?	☐	☐
Is my report approximately 100 words in length?	☐	☐
Have I excluded irrelevant material such as planning, graphs, data analysis, interpretation, conclusions or evaluations?	☐	☐

Table of Data

	YES	NO
Have I provided a specific title(s) for my table(s)?	☐	☐
Have I included units of measurement for all variables?	☐	☐
Have I used ICT for effective presentation?	☐	☐
Have I tabulated data relevant to the stated aim/hypotheses of the fieldwork report?	☐	☐
Have I excluded statistical analysis, such as Spearman's Rank calculations, mean etc?	☐	☐
Is there adequate data presented to allow for a thorough investigation of the stated aim and to allow for statistical testing?	☐	☐

Exam Tip

Having conducted all fieldwork data collection activities and completed the student checklist for the examination submission materials, it is necessary to prepare for Section A of AS1. Tables 1 and 2 provide essential key questions relating to fieldwork preparation and follow-through which require careful consideration.

Table 1: Key questions relating to Fieldwork Planning	
Stages within the investigation process	**Key Questions**
Formulation of AIM	How does the aim of the study link to the theoretical content of AS1/AS2 units of study? What are the hypotheses/sub-aims? What is their purpose within the investigation?
Selection of... **LOCATION/ SITE**	What site(s) were selected for study? What factors influenced this choice? How did the physical, human or environmental geography of the area influence site selection?
Planning for... **HEALTH & SAFETY**	What is meant by a risk assessment and how/when/why was it conducted? What specific hazards were identified in the chosen site? What contingencies were planned and adopted to manage risks?
Planning for... **DATA COLLECTION**	What variables were identified for primary data collection, in relation to the aim of the study? What equipment or materials were required for primary data collection? What is meant by pilot testing and why is this an essential part of pre-fieldwork planning? What secondary data sources were identified as relevant for the investigation?
Planning for... **SAMPLING**	What is sampling? Why is it essential to employ sampling in the field? What **method** of sampling (random, systematic, stratified or pragmatic) is required for data collection? What **size** of sample is required? What justification can be provided for the chosen sample size and method?

Table 2: Key questions relating to Data Collection and Fieldwork Follow-up	
Stages within the investigation process	**Key Questions**
DATA COLLECTION	What methods/procedures were employed to collect primary/secondary data? What steps were taken to ensure that reliable/accurate data was collected? What is the precise role/purpose of secondary data collected?
GRAPHICAL REPRESENTATION	Why is graphical representation an essential stage in the investigation process? What method(s) of graphical representation were selected to display data? What justification can be provided for the chosen methods? What are the potential limitations of such techniques?
DATA ANALYSIS/ INTERPRETATION	What trends, if any, are displayed from the data in relation to the aim of the study? What residual/anomalous values can be identified, if any?
STATISTICAL ANALYSIS	What is the purpose of using statistics within geographical studies? What statistical method(s) were employed? Why was this statistical method appropriate for the investigation? What statistical interpretation can be developed and how significant are results? Can hypotheses be accepted/rejected as a result of statistical analysis?
GEOGRAPHICAL CONCLUSION	What are the overall findings of the investigation in relation to the aim of the study? Do results conform/conflict with theoretical expectations?
EVALUATION	In critical reflection, what strengths/weaknesses can be identified? What factors may have influenced the reliability of the results and conclusions? Are there any obvious ways in which the investigation could be modified or improved? How could the investigation be extended to allow for a deeper level of geographical understanding?

2 Data Collection

2.1 Sampling

Population is the term used to describe the complete set of items to be investigated. It is often impossible, impractical and unnecessary to study the entire 'population', so geographers commonly use the process of **sampling** to reduce the numerical quantity or areal coverage to be studied. Sampling is therefore employed to select a **portion** of the total population from which valid statistical inferences can be derived. This portion selected is commonly referred to as the **sample**. For example, if a geographer aims to investigate whether river variables change with distance downstream, it is impossible to study the entire course of the river. The geographer may decide to focus on a number of carefully selected sites which form the **sample**.

Sample Selection: key considerations

There are a number of important factors to be considered when deriving a sample population.

- **Sample Size** – The sample size must be sufficiently large to gain a **representative** view of the total population. Geographical conclusions will lack validity if they are based on an inadequate sample size. In statistical theory most data conforms to a normal distribution which, when plotted, produces a symmetrical bell-shaped curve (Figure 4). A large proportion of the values lie close to the mean with a decreasing proportion dispersed further from the mean. Geographers need to be aware that, for the sample population to be representative, it should reflect the characteristics of the normal distribution curve. This is more probable if the sample population is large. A high level of representation is achieved if the mean of the sample population closely approximates, or equates with, the mean of the total population.

Figure 4 The normal distribution curve

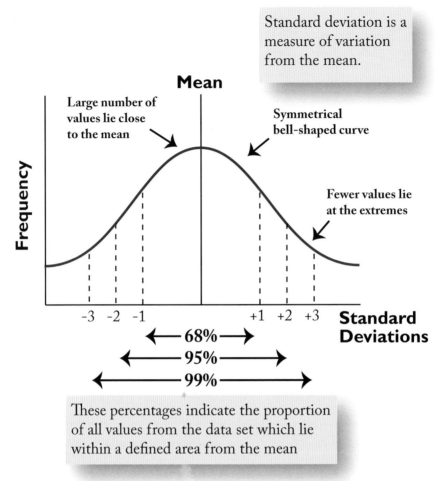

Standard deviation is a measure of variation from the mean.

Mean

Large number of values lie close to the mean

Symmetrical bell-shaped curve

Fewer values lie at the extremes

Frequency

-3 -2 -1   +1 +2 +3 **Standard Deviations**

←— 68% —→
←——— 95% ———→
←———— 99% ————→

These percentages indicate the proportion of all values from the data set which lie within a defined area from the mean

- **Elimination of bias** – To obtain an **accurate** and **representative** sample the researcher needs to eliminate bias by carefully considering the characteristics of the population. For example, a survey which investigates residents' perception of a proposed leisure complex in their locality would be biased and unrepresentative if the sample concentrated mainly on a specific age sector of the population.

- **Type of sampling procedure** – It is necessary to consider which type of sampling procedure would be most appropriate for the type of investigation. There are four main types (outlined in Figure 5), but geographers frequently use a combination of each to fulfil successfully the aim of their study.

Figure 5 Sampling procedures

Point sampling

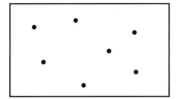

Individual **points**, or sites, are selected for investigation, eg sites along the course of a river, or a vegetation sampling quadrat which uses pins to locate points.

Grid or area sampling

This involves delimiting an **area** for study. The size of the area varies according to the nature of the investigation, eg a quadrat is generally a $0.25m^2$ area used for vegetation sampling.

Line or transect sampling

A **line** is plotted, along which data collection will occur. This is generally selected by geographers when variables under investigation are expected to demonstrate a progressive variation spatially, eg ecological succession studies, soil catena studies, etc.

Belt sampling

An **area** along a line is defined for investigation. This is also a useful method for vegetation and soil studies when the geographical aim involves a wider areal focus compared to transect studies.

• **Type of sampling method** – Researchers also need to consider the most appropriate sampling method to yield reliable information in relation to the aim of the enquiry. There are three recommended types of sampling method – random, systematic and stratified sampling. These methods are summarised in Figure 6.

Figure 6 Types of sampling methods

	Random	Systematic	Stratified
Description	Random sampling involves selecting a sample using a random number generator, eg a random number table or the random number function on a calculator. Theoretically every member of the total population should have an equal chance of being selected. In spatial studies, sites can be located using the random numbers which can relate to co-ordinates which will inter-connect on a gridded map.	Systematic sampling involves the selection of data using a pre-determined interval. As with all sampling methods, this process can involve points, areas, lines or belts, eg it may involve interviewing every second householder along a street or studying soil at every 10m interval along a hill slope transect.	Stratified sampling is useful when sub-groups or subsets are clearly identified within the total population. This method should ensure proportional representation of each sub-group in relation to the total population, eg in a land use survey, where it is known that 70% of the study area is comprised of sandy soil and 30% clay soil, if 100 points are surveyed, 70 should be in the sandy zone and 30 on the clay.
Advantages	• The procedure is totally objective and should thus be unbiased. • If the sample size is sufficiently large, the data should be representative of the total population (reflecting the normal distribution). • Random numbers are easily generated for pre-fieldwork planning.	• This method is relatively simple, easy to employ and allows for well-organised data collection in the field. • It is particularly appropriate for studies which require an even coverage over time or distance, as it affords the researcher a degree of control over the data selection process.	• Conclusions are likely to be more valid when geographical sub-groups have been represented. • The method allows for flexibility as random, or systematic sampling can be used to select the data within the proportional sub-groups.
Disadvantages	• It does not take into account any underlying strata, or subsets, within the population. Therefore one grouping may be under, or over, represented. • The sampling can produce 'bunching' which is unsuitable for studies which aim to investigate a progressive spatial or temporal dimension.	• There is a higher chance of bias as the individual decides the interval and not all points/areas have an equal chance of selection. • It is possible that an underlying pattern could be missed and thus the total population may be misrepresented.	• If a multitude of sub-groups are inherent in the total population, then stratified sampling can become rather complex. • If strata are inappropriately identified, then the sample will not be truly representative and conclusions will be erroneous.

Pragmatic sampling

Although an improper procedure, a pragmatic approach is sometimes employed when significant constraints exist within the physical or human environment.

Such constraints may include the occurrence of hazardous sites, the lack of landowner permission or restricted access.

A pragmatic approach may thus involve the selection of a more flexible model which may be necessary to avoid such constraints. In a river study a pragmatic approach may involve the selection of only safe or accessible sites downstream.

Advantages

- Although limited advantages exist, it may be necessary to deviate from more rigorous sampling methods for practical reasons such as risk avoidance.
- If the study objectives are adhered to, a pragmatic approach should yield data which can be processed and subsequently it may be possible to make reasoned judgements or estimations.

Disadvantages

In a scientific hypothesis testing approach, there are significant limitations which must be recognised.

- Selection bias is an obvious problem as the sample is controlled by the researcher on the basis of certain characteristics. The approach thus lacks absolute objectivity as sites are generated in a non-random way.
- As this method is less rigorous, data accuracy, validity and thus statistical reliability are compromised.
- There can be no assurance that data will be representative as it is highly probable that results may be influenced by distortion.

2.2 Vegetation sampling

Almost all ecological studies involve an element of vegetation sampling. Geographers widely use a **quadrat** to obtain a vegetation sample for measurement.

What is a quadrat?

A quadrat is a defined area of vegetation for ecological study. Quadrats vary in size depending on the type of vegetation unit. Although quadrats are traditionally, and commonly, square they can vary in shape.

Why use a quadrat?

There are many characteristics of vegetation which can be measured using the quadrat.

- **Vegetation cover** – this is the proportion of the ground occupied by a particular species, usually expressed as a percentage of the total quadrat area.

- **Vegetation frequency** – the chance of finding a species with one throw of a quadrat in a study area. If a species has a frequency of 50% it should occur in five of every ten quadrats analysed.

- **Biodiversity** – the number of species which occur within the defined quadrat area. This may be recorded as a numerical value or plant identification can provide more detail on the floral composition of the quadrat area.
  An alternative, but more subjective, assessment of vegetation abundance can make use of a devised key, which aims to simplify the data recording process. Some subjective scales commonly used to measure plant abundance are illustrated in Figure 7.

Figure 7 DAFOR Scale

The DAFOR scale can use the following descriptive terms: **D**ominant, **A**bundant, **F**requent, **O**ccasional, **R**are. Obviously these terms are open to subjective interpretation, a weakness which must be recognised by the researcher. An alternative approach, based on the **Braun-Blanquet** method which has cover and abundance scales, is shown below:

Cover	Description
*	Sparsely or very sparsely present, cover small
1	Plentiful but of small cover value
2	Very numerous or covering at least 5% of area
3	Any number of individuals covering 25–50% of area
4	Any number of individuals covering 50–75% of area
5	Covering more than 75% of area

Abundance	Description
1	Growing singly, isolated individuals
2	Grouped or tufted
3	In patches or cushions
4	In small colonies, extensive patches or in carpets
5	Pure population

Eg, a species described as 2.2 would cover 5% of the area and grow in groups or tufts.

Size of quadrat

Ecologists need to consider the size of the quadrat to ensure that the data is representative. The chosen quadrat size should be based on the size of the plant communities and their distribution pattern. Figure 8 illustrates recommended quadrat sizes for different plant communities.

Figure 8 Recommended quadrat sizes

Lichen and moss communities

0.5m 0.5m

Grassland/dwarf heathland

1-2m 1-2m

Shrubby heathland/tall grassland

2-4m 2-4m

Scrub woodland/shrubs

10m 10m

Woodland Canopies

20-40m 20-40m

Types of quadrat

There are three main types of quadrat which are most frequently used in ecological studies. These are outlined in Figure 9.

Figure 9 Types of quadrat

	Frame Quadrat	Grid Quadrat	Point Quadrat
Characteristics	Frame quadrats are generally home-made, using four pegs carefully measured to represent the corners, with string to define the study area.	Grid quadrats are frames with the area sub-divided into 100 units to facilitate measurement.	A narrow frame with holes allows 10 pins through to indicate the points which record species as "hits". Unlike the grid and frame quadrat, it does not use an area approach. Pins can be adjusted to the height of the vegetation.
Advantages	• Useful when larger quadrat size is essential. • Do not flatten vegetation, producing a more accurate assessment of vegetation cover.	• The grid can make floristic assessment of cover more accurate. • Easily transported and quicker to use.	• Useful method to determine strata when vegetation is tall or multi-layered. • Vegetation is not flattened allowing for greater accuracy.
Disadvantages	• Estimations can be subjective without a grid to minimise error. • Difficult and time-consuming to construct.	• Tall vegetation can be crushed which can influence measurements. In an assessment of biodiversity, less significant species can thus be hidden.	• It does not allow for an assessment of cover, so the occurrence of minor species may be missed.

2.3 Questionnaires

What is a questionnaire?

- A questionnaire is a predetermined list of questions used by a researcher to obtain primary data relevant to the aim of a chosen study.
- It can be relatively simple, with questions to secure basic factual details, or it can be more complex, exploring public perceptions, attitudes and values relating to a geographical theme.

Designing a questionnaire

Questionnaire design involves considerable planning to ensure that questions are unambiguous and capture all aspects of information relevant to the chosen field study.

Take Note

The final analysis and conclusion is only as good as the data collected.

Plan and collect carefully.

Planning a questionnaire

Figure 10 Types of questions

Type of question	Advantages	Disadvantages
Closed These offer the respondent a fixed range of answers, usually with mutually exclusive options.	• Less time consuming to complete. • Answers lend themselves to quantitative analysis and the application of statistics.	• Unsuitable if public attitudes or perceptions are required. • They tend to be restrictive and inflexible as answers are predetermined.
Open Questions which offer the respondent the opportunity to outline their views or perceptions and formulate their own style of response.	• Respondents are is able to present their ideas without having to select from predetermined categories. Therefore data is likely to be more accurate.	• Difficult to collate and present in graphical or diagrammatic form. • Involves subjective interpretation by the researcher.
Likert Scales These are scales which allow the respondent to rank their attitude or view along a predetermined continuum.	• Numerical values can be produced, making graphical and statistical analysis possible. • Intensity/strength of feeling can be captured.	• Analysis can be complex and tedious if an expansive continuum is employed to cope with positive and negative views.

Question relevance

All questions included should capture information relevant to the aim of the study.

Length/Structure

The questions should be short, as respondents will be hesitant if the survey is time-consuming. The questionnaire should have well organised categories with clear, concise instructions.

Sampling

It may be necessary to consider:
1 Sample size – A larger sample size will ensure more reliable data.
2 Sampling method – It is important to choose the appropriate sampling method when administering the questionnaire eg random, systematic, stratified (refer to section 2.1).

What should be considered when designing and administering a questionnaire?

Pilot study

A pilot study should be conducted on a small percentage of the sample population. This allows the questions to be 'road tested' for accuracy and ambiguity. Evaluation of the pilot study may make modification of the questionnaire necessary.

Avoid personal questions

It is not good practice to ask direct questions of a personal nature, eg income, age, religion etc.

Avoiding bias

It is often necessary to consider factors which may influence the data. eg obtaining a cross-section of the population to avoid over-representation of a distinct group which would introduce bias.

Type of questions

The type of questions needs to be carefully chosen. There are possible alternatives which include – Open, Closed and Likert scales (see Figure 10).

Figure 11 Analysing questionnaire design

Visitor Survey

I am an A level geography student and I am conducting some research into human use of this coastal area. I would value your opinion and I would be grateful if you would take a few minutes to help me with my research.

Brief introduction to explain the purpose of the research.

Survey Number _____

Date _____

Time _____

Weather _____

Personal Details

Age: ☐ <20 ☐ 21-35 ☐ 36-50 ☐ 51-65 ☐ >65

Sex: ☐ Male ☐ Female

Personal questions which can be completed by the researcher without asking the interviewee.

1. Have you ever visited this site before? ☐ Yes ☐ No

Begin with a simple, closed ended question.

2. How far did you travel to get here today?

☐ <1km ☐ 5-9.9km ☐ >20km
☐ 1-4.9km ☐ 10-20km

*Question 2 is an example of a **closed-ended question**. The respondent can select from the options provided.*

3. How did you travel here today?

☐ Foot ☐ Car ☐ Train
☐ Bus ☐ Cycle ☐ Other (specify) _____

4. Did you visit the beach for any of the following reasons?

☐ Walking ☐ Dog walking ☐ Picnicking
☐ Horse riding ☐ Swimming ☐ Cycling
☐ Photography ☐ Sun bathing ☐ Sightseeing
☐ Other (specify) _____

*Always include '**other**' to cover alternative possibilities.*

5. Do you consider this area to be: (tick where appropriate)

	Excellent					Poor	
	5	4	3	2	1	0	
Beautiful							Ugly
Unspoilt							Spoilt
Quiet							Noisy
Clean							Dirty
Safe							Unsafe

*Question 5 is an example of a '**Likert scale**' question. The respondent can tick the column to present the **strength** of their perception of the area.*

6. Which management schemes from the list below have you seen today?

☐ Litter bins ☐ Education Boards ☐ Pathways
☐ Fenced off areas ☐ None ☐ Other _____

7. Would you like to suggest any improvements to the area?

_____

_____

_____

*Question 7 is an example of an **open-ended question**. The respondent can formulate their own answer.*

3 Statistical Methods

Geographical data is often complex and lengthy, making interpretation difficult. It can be simplified and reduced into a concise mathematical form – this involves calculating **statistics**. Once statistics are clearly understood they are invaluable in helping to summarise, or interpret, aspects of geographical data.

3.1 Measures of central tendency

In any data set an average value can be obtained to represent the 'centre' of the distribution. The three most commonly used measures are:

• The **mean**

• The **median**

• The **mode**

The value of each statistic is outlined in Figure 13 , and its application demonstrated using the geographical data presented in Figure 12.

Figure 12

Geographical data

A group of students, carrying out a fieldwork river study, obtained the following data for bedload size, randomly sampled at one site along a river.

Long axis of rock particle (cm)

5.7	5.7	14.1	15
15.1	16.7	21.4	32.6

26

Take Note

- All 3 measures of average have their own strengths and weaknesses which need to be understood if their 'usefulness' is to be fully appreciated.

- As they vary considerably within the same data set, the analysis and comparison of all three measures of average can provide a deeper understanding of the data.

Figure 13 Measures of Central Tendency – Summary Fact Sheet

Statistic	Application/ Calculation	Advantages	Limitations
Mean	The mean (or arithmetic mean) is obtained by totalling all the values making up the data set and dividing by the total number of values in the data set. Formula: $\bar{x} = \dfrac{\sum x}{n}$ where: $\bar{x}$ = mean $\sum$ = sum of x = value in data set n = number of values in data set	• It is an accurate measure of central tendency as all values are considered in the equation. • It is relatively simple to calculate and its value is commonly appreciated. • It is most reliable when there are many values in the data set and there are no abnormally extreme values.	• It is influenced by extreme values in the data set. • It may yield a decimal figure which can be inappropriate depending on the geographical context, eg an answer of 14.6 persons. • Reliability is reduced by small sample size.

Worked example

$\bar{x}$ = (5.7+5.7+14.1+15+15.1+16.7+21.4+32.6) ÷ 8

$\bar{x}$ = 126.3 ÷ 8 = 15.7875

Statistic	Application/ Calculation	Advantages	Limitations
Median	The median is the mid-point in a set of values when they are arranged in order of size (ranked numerically).	• It is a more preferable representation of the 'centre' of the distribution if the data contains values at the extremes. • It can be more reliable when there is 'bunching', or clustering of values in the data set.	• It is mathematically a less accurate average since the actual values do not form part of a calculation. • It is less reliable when there are few values in the data set or when there are large gaps between the values.

Worked example

5.7, 5.7, 14.1, 15, ◯ 15.1, 16.7, 21.4, 32.6

Median is 4½th value = 15.05   (15+15.1) ÷ 2

Statistic	Application/ Calculation	Advantages	Limitations
Mode	This is the value which occurs most frequently in the data set. A data set may have no identifiable mode.	• The mode does serve a useful purpose in describing the general shape of the distribution, eg unimodal (having one mode) or bimodal (having two modal classes) . • It is fast and easy to work out as there is no calculation involved.	• It is of limited value as a mathematical measure of central tendency as the modal value may represent extreme values within the data set, as indicated in the worked example. • It does not take into consideration the spread of the values within the data set.

Worked example – data is UNIMODAL

5.7, 5.7, 14.1, 15, 15.1, 16.7, 21.4, 32.6

Mode = 5.7

3.2 Measures of dispersion

The mean, as we have seen, summarises the 'centre' of a distribution in a relatively simple way. On its own, however, it is often not informative enough. **Dispersion** from the mean can provide a valuable insight into the data set and allows for fuller geographical comparisons.

Dispersion from the mean can be obtained by using three main statistical measures:
• The range
• The inter-quartile range
• Standard deviation

Although other measures of dispersion exist, only a knowledge of the **range** is essential.

Range

This is the simplest measure of spread – it is merely the difference between the lowest and highest values in the data set.

Advantages
• The range is easy to calculate and illustrates the **spread** of the data in the sample population.
• When used with the mean it can provide an insight into the distribution of values around the mean – it therefore develops the statistical usefulness of the mean.

Long axis of rock particle (cm)

| 5.7 | 5.7 | 14.1 | 15 |
| 15.1 | 16.7 | 21.4 | 32.6 |

Highest value – Lowest value = Range

| 32.6 | – | 5.7 | = | 26.9 |

Limitations
• It is of limited use since it depends only on **two** values and ignores the distribution of all values in between. It is particularly disadvantageous if the extreme values are atypical.
• A general disadvantage is that the range of a sample population tends to increase as the sample size increases.

3.3 Correlation

Statistics, so far, have been concerned with single variable data sets, but in many investigations it is necessary to study the **relationship** between variables.

Key terms

Correlation – is used to describe the degree of association, or link, between two sets of variables.

Scattergraphs – can be used to graphically present the relationship between two variables. The types of relationship are illustrated in Figure 14.

Independent variable – or 'control' variable, is plotted on the horizontal 'x' axis of the scattergraph.

Dependent variable – the variable which is expected to be influenced by the control variable, is plotted on the vertical 'y' axis.

Line of best fit – this line can be plotted on a scattergraph to show the best possible trend. It can be estimated subjectively by eye but is much more accurate and objective when calculated mathematically.

Residual value – this is a point which lies at a distance from the line of best fit. It is often referred to as an **anomaly**.

Figure 14 Types of correlation

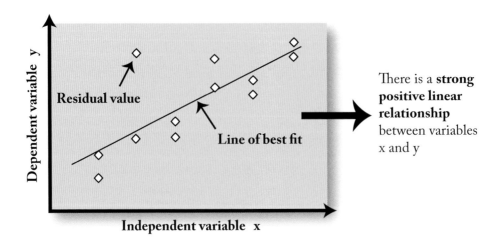

Dependent variable y

Residual value

Line of best fit

Independent variable x

There is a **strong positive linear relationship** between variables x and y

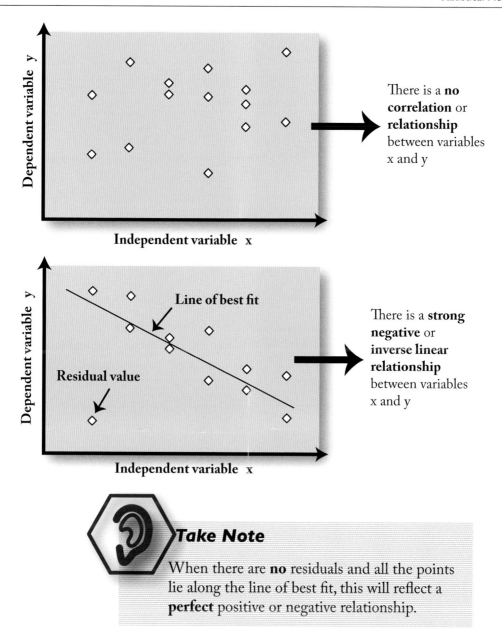

There is a **no correlation** or **relationship** between variables x and y

There is a **strong negative** or **inverse linear relationship** between variables x and y

Take Note

When there are **no** residuals and all the points lie along the line of best fit, this will reflect a **perfect** positive or negative relationship.

Spearman's rank correlation coefficient (r_s)

This is a statistical test which will provide a **reliable** measure of the **degree of association** between two sets of variables.

It will provide a numerical value which can be used to assess the **strength** of the linear relationship as well as the **type** of relationship, positive or negative, between the two sets of variables.

Calculation of r_s value

Formula:

$$r_s = 1 - \left(\frac{6 \Sigma d^2}{n^3 - n} \right)$$

where   d = the difference in rank of the values of each matched pair

n = the number of ranked pairs

Σ = the sum of

Worked Example

Hypothesis – There is a significant increase in river discharge downstream.

River site	x distance down-stream (km)	y River discharge (cumecs)	Rank x	Rank y	Difference in ranks d	d^2
1	0	0.26	12	11	1	1
2	0.4	0.15	11	12	-1	1
3	0.8	0.38	10	9.5	0.5	0.25
4	2.2	0.38	9	9.5	-0.5	0.25
5	2.6	1.62	8	8	0	0
6	3.0	1.93	7	5	2	4
7	3.4	1.95	6	4	2	4
8	3.8	1.92	5	6	-1	1
9	4.2	2.12	4	2	2	4
10	4.6	2.06	3	3	0	0
11	5.0	1.80	2	7	-5	25
12	5.4	2.70	1	1	0	0

$\Sigma d^2 = 40.5$

Steps

1. Rank the independent variable x from highest to lowest.

2. Rank the dependent variable y in a similar way.

3. Two or more identical values are given tied ranks.

4. Calculate the difference in ranks (d) for each pair of values.

5. Square each difference to remove all negative values (d²).

6. Total all the d² values to obtain Σ d².

7. Complete the calculation using the formula to determine the r_s value.

8. Interpret the rs value using the significance graph or table in Figure 15 (pages 35–36).

$$(r_s) = 1 - \left(\frac{6 \Sigma d^2}{n^3 - n} \right)$$

$$(r_s) = 1 - \frac{6 \times 40.5}{12^3 - 12}$$

$$(r_s) = 1 - \frac{243}{1716}$$

$$(r_s) = 1 - 0.14 = 0.86$$

Statistical interpretation

The **calculated** r_s value of 0.86 exceeds the **critical** value of 0.77 at the 99% significance level with 10 degrees of freedom. Therefore river discharge increases **significantly** downstream.

Interpretation of (r_s)

Increasing significance　　　　　　　　**Increasing significance**

-1 ⬅　　　　　　0　　　➡ +1

Perfect Negative　　**No Correlation**　　**Perfect Positive**
Linear Relationship　　　　　　　　**Linear Relationship**

Therefore the r_s value will lie on a scale between +1 (perfect positive relationship) and −1 (perfect negative relationship). However we need to know whether any particular r_s value is close enough numerically to 1 to be considered significant.

Statistical significance

When investigating the link, or association, between two sets of variables, there is always the possibility that the relationship may have occurred by **chance**. Statisticians state that a greater than 5% possibility that the relationship occurred by chance is unacceptable to establish reliable significance. This means that the relationship may have occurred by chance more than 5 times out of 100. Therefore 5% is the level that geographers use as the **rejection level**.

How can the level of significance be determined?

In order to determine if the **calculated r_s value** is significant, and at what level, it is necessary to consult a **significance graph** or a **significance table**. (Figure 15)

Steps

1. Work out the **degrees of freedom** (n–2) and find this value on the horizontal axis of the significance graph.

2. Where the degrees of freedom line intersects with the 5% probability line on the significance graph – read across to the vertical axis to obtain the **critical rs value.**

3. If the **calculated** r_s value **exceeds** the **critical** r_s value, then the relationship is significant at the 5% probability level.

4. To check for a higher level of significance a similar method can be employed making use of the 1% and 0.1% probability lines to obtain critical values.

Figure 15 Spearman's rank correlation coefficient (r_s) Significance Graph

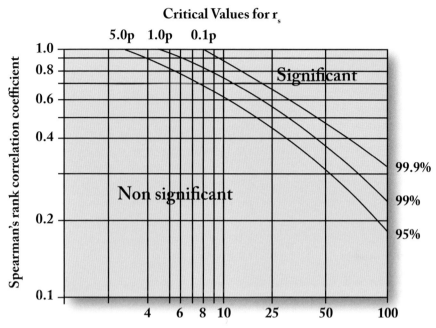

Degrees of freedom [Number of ranked pairs (n) −2]

95% significance level (5.0p)
This means that the relation-ship may have occurred by chance 5 times out of 100. This is a critical level of significance to achieve if the relationship is to be stated as significant with a acceptable degree of reliablity.

99% significance level (1.0p)
This means that the relation-ship may have occurred by chance only 1 time out of 100. This level, if achieved, provides a more reliable relationship than the 95% level.

99.9% significance level (0.1p)
This level indicates a highly significant relationship. There is only 1 chance out of 1000 that the association may have occurred by chance.

Spearman's rank correlation coefficient (r_s) Significance Table

Critical values of Spearman's rank correlation coefficient, r_s		
Significance Level		
Degrees of freedom	0.05 (5%)	0.01 (1%)
4	0.88	1.00
5	0.83	0.96
6	0.80	0.91
7	0.77	0.87
8	0.72	0.84
9	0.68	0.80
10	0.64	0.77
11	0.60	0.74
12	0.57	0.71
15	0.50	0.65
20	0.47	0.59
25	0.44	0.54
30	0.39	0.48
40	0.35	0.43
50	0.31	0.38

Take Note

• Spearman's Rank Correlation test can be used on data which consists of discrete variables (raw figures), or percentages, which can be ranked.

• The data should have at least 10 sets of paired values for the test to be statistically reliable.

• A significant value of r_s only indicates a strong degree of association between the variables. It does **not** prove that there is any **causal** link between them. In other words, the fact that two phenomena illustrate a positive, or inverse, trend is an indication that there **may** be a causative link which can be explored with further investigation.

3.4 Nearest neighbour analysis

The Nearest Neighbour statistic (Rn) is used to provide an objective measure of the distribution **pattern** of points arranged spatially in the landscape. In geography these points may relate to settlements, buildings, plants, springs, quarries, farms etc.

A numerical score is obtained from statistical analysis, which will allow the geographer to determine, with a degree of reliability, if the pattern is significantly
• **random**
• **clustered**
• **regular**

The calculated Rn numerical value will lie between **0** and **2.15**. Figure 16 provides an illustration of how the value can be interpreted.

We need to know if the values are close enough to **0, 1**, or **2.15** to indicate if the distribution pattern is significantly clustered, random or regular, with an acceptable degree of reliability. Therefore statistical analysis and interpretation are necessary to provide an objective and accurate conclusion.

Figure 16 Interpretation of Nearest Neighbour Value

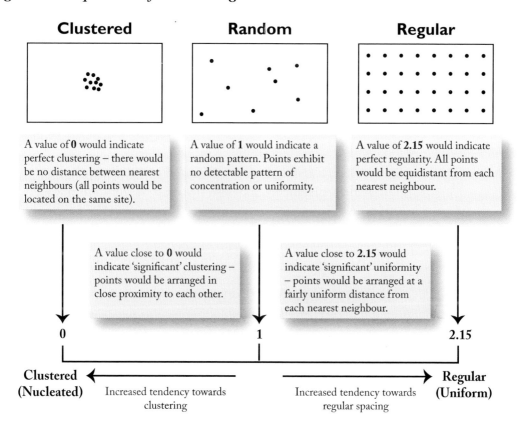

Clustered

Random

Regular

A value of **0** would indicate perfect clustering – there would be no distance between nearest neighbours (all points would be located on the same site).

A value of **1** would indicate a random pattern. Points exhibit no detectable pattern of concentration or uniformity.

A value of **2.15** would indicate perfect regularity. All points would be equidistant from each nearest neighbour.

A value close to **0** would indicate 'significant' clustering – points would be arranged in close proximity to each other.

A value close to **2.15** would indicate 'significant' uniformity – points would be arranged at a fairly uniform distance from each nearest neighbour.

0

1

2.15

**Clustered
(Nucleated)** ← Increased tendency towards clustering

Increased tendency towards regular spacing → **Regular
(Uniform)**

Worked Example

A geographer analysing the distribution pattern of post offices in Belfast (Figure 17 opposite), theoretically expected a random pattern. The expectation was based on the assumption that this low order service would not require a high threshold population to sustain economic viability and would therefore be located randomly in community, or neighbourhood, areas.

$$Rn = 2\bar{d} \sqrt{\frac{n}{A}}$$

where $\bar{d}$ = the mean distance between nearest neighbours

n = the number of points

A = the area under study

Steps

1. The points in the study area are accurately mapped and annotated with a number (Figure 17).

2. A table is constructed to record the straight line distance between each point (post offices in this example) and its nearest neighbour (Figure 18).

3. The average distance $(\bar{d})$ is calculated by totalling all the individual distance values and dividing by the total number of points.

4. The study area is then calculated (A).

5. The Rn numerical value is then calculated by substituting these values into the statistical formula (as illustrated in worked example Figure 18).

6. In order to interpret the Rn value, it is necessary to consult the Nearest Neighbour Significance Graph (Figure 19).

Figure 17 Post Office distribution in Belfast: Nearest Neighbour Analysis

Figure 18 Post Offices in Belfast – Nearest Neighbours

WorkedExample

Post Office	Nearest Neighbour	Distance (km)	Post Office	Nearest Neighbour	Distance (km)
1	2	1.22	28	27	0.44
2	1	1.22	29	28	1.22
3	15	1.00	30	28	1.00
4	5	0.44	31	32	1.33
5	4	0.44	32	31	1.33
6	7	0.67	33	35	1.11
7	6	0.67	34	35	1.22
8	10	0.56	35	33	1.11
9	10	0.67	36	37	0.78
10	8	0.56	37	38	0.44
11	12	0.44	38	37	0.44
12	11	0.44	39	38	1.11
13	11	1.11	40	51	1.00
14	15	1.22	41	42	0.33
15	3	1.00	42	41	0.33
16	17	0.89	43	44	0.33
17	16	0.89	44	43	0.33
18	17	1.00	45	46	0.67
19	16	1.00	46	45	0.67
20	21	2.22	47	48	1.44
21	26	1.22	48	47	1.44
22	23	0.89	49	46	0.67
23	24	0.44	50	44	0.44
24	23	0.44	51	40	1.00
25	27	1.11	52	53	0.67
26	25	1.44	53	52	0.67
27	28	0.44	54	47	3.56

Calculation of Rn numerical value

$$Rn = 2\bar{d}\sqrt{\frac{n}{A}}$$

$$Rn = 2 \times 0.902\sqrt{\frac{54}{144}}$$

$$Rn = 1.804 \sqrt{0.375}$$

$$Rn = 1.105$$

Area = 144 km²

Σd = 48.72

$\bar{d}$ = 0.902

Interpretation of Rn value

With 54 points a value of 1.105 indicates a **significantly random** distribution.

Figure 19 Nearest neighbour significance graph

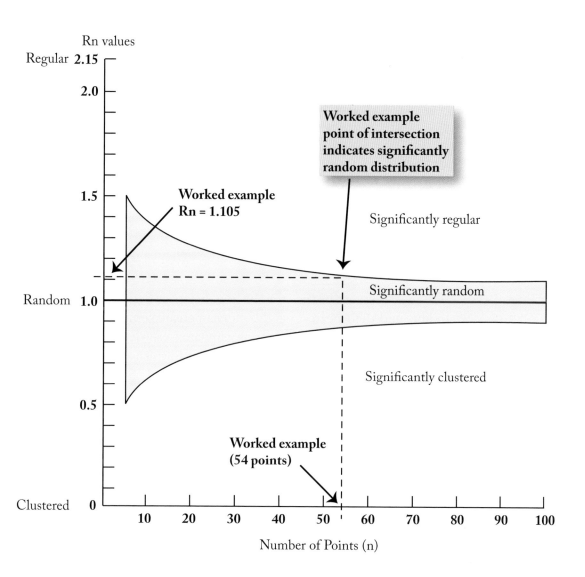

Locate the precise number of points on the x axis and the calculated Rn value on the y axis. Their point of intersection on the graph will determine whether the pattern can be classified as significantly:

• Random
• Regular
• Clustered

Take Note

Nearest Neighbour Analysis is a very useful statistic when analysing geographical distribution patterns, but the following points need to be considered.

- Statisticians state that a minimum of 30 points are required to ensure reliability and validity of conclusions.

- The delineation of the boundary of the area will require very careful consideration. A larger area will lower the Rn value and exaggerate the extent of clustering. Conversely the inclusion of a smaller area will increase the Rn value and exaggerate the extent of regularity. The total area is therefore critical to the statistical outcome.

- The measurement of the straight line distances between points and their nearest neighbours can create some problems. For example, if the points relate to settlements it may be difficult to locate the centre point for measurement, especially if the settlement has a linear morphology.

- The inability of the statistic to classify a linear pattern can be regarded as a limitation. For example, settlements are often distributed in a linear fashion as a result of relief, drainage, communications or other topographical landscape features. Therefore the application of nearest neighbour analysis may result in a misleading statistical interpretation.

- Although the nearest neighbour statistic provides a reliable classification of pattern (to a 5% probability level) it provides no explanation for the distribution. Geographers need to complete further research to explore potential geographical reasons for the patterns classified.

3.5 Chi-squared statistic

The Chi-squared test or χ^2 is used to find the significance of the difference between one frequency distribution and, usually, the frequency distribution expected by chance. It can only be used when the data are in the form of counted groups or frequencies. In other words, if you collected data and put them into classes (0-5, 5.1-10, 10.1-15 and so on) you would be able to compare these frequencies with those that would have occurred by chance.

Worked Example

For example, in a study of particle size along a river, if you had collected information from 3 points along a river, taking 30 particles from each site, measured the three axes and found the average and then grouped them into size categories, you might end up with a table like the one below.

In this case the fact that one of the particles at Point 1 had an average size of 1.7 cms is not recorded; it is classed as one of the six particles in this class at that point of the river. These are called **observed values**.

Particle size at three points on a river

Particle size/ River Points	Point 1	Point 2	Point 3	Total
>5cm	12	6	6	24
2.6 – 5cm	12	10	6	28
≤2.5cm	6	14	18	38
Total	30	30	30	90

At Point 3 there were six particles larger than 5 cms

Row total

Column total

Grand total

Hypothesis and null hypothesis

We want to know whether there is a difference between particle size at various points downstream. In order to ensure objectivity, a geographer will test a **null hypothesis**. This states that there are no differences (in our case in particle size at the different points sampled) other than might occur by chance. The symbol H_0 is used to abbreviate the null hypothesis in statistics. The null hypothesis here would be: '**There is no significant difference between particle sizes at various points downstream other than might occur by chance**'. We can also make a **hypothesis** (H_1) which in this case would be 'There is a significant difference between particle sizes at various points downstream'. It is always useful in Chi-squared tests to state the null hypothesis and the hypothesis before the test is carried out. It is always the null hypothesis which is tested – we are trying to prove ourselves wrong. This should produce a fairer result than if we were trying to prove ourselves correct.

Expected values

A Chi-squared test will compare this distribution of classes or frequencies, usually with what the distribution would have been if it had come about by chance. The chance figures for each cell of the frequency table are easily calculated. The table on page 41 shows that just 6 of the pebbles at Point 2 were over 5 centimetres in size. Since 24 out of the 90 particles in total were over that size, we would expect, if the results had occurred by chance, that there would be 8 pebbles of that size at points 1, 2 and 3.

To calculate the chance occurrence of each cell, multiply the row total by the column total and divide by the grand total eg (24 x 30) ÷ 90 = 8.0. This will provide the **expected values**.

Particle size at three points along a river with expected sizes according to chance

Particle size/River points	Point 1		Point 2		Point 3		Total
>5 cm	12	8.0	6	8.0	6	8.0	24
2.6–5 cm	12	9.3	10	9.3	6	9.3	28
≤2.5 cm	6	12.7	14	12.7	18	12.7	38
Total	30		30		30		90

Observed value

Expected value

$$\frac{38 \times 30}{90} = 12.7$$

Calculation

This is the Chi-squared formula.

$$\chi^2 = \Sigma \frac{(O-E)^2}{E}$$

The bigger the difference between the observed figures and the expected figures, the bigger the chance of the difference being found significant. For each cell calculate the expected figure and put it in the table in one corner of each cell. Apply the formula with the square of the difference between the observed and the expected figures divided by the expected for each cell and then add them together. The total figure provides the Chi-squared statistic, as the worked example below shows.

Chi-squared statistic $= [(12 - 8.0)^2 \div 8.0] + [(6 - 8.0)^2 \div 8.0] + [(6.0 - 8.0)^2 \div 8.0]$

$+ [(12 - 9.3)^2 \div 9.3] + [(10 - 9.3)^2 \div 9.3] + [(6 - 9.3)^2 \div 9.3]$

$+ [(6 - 12.7)^2 \div 12.7] + [(14 - 12.7)^2 \div 12.7] + [(18 - 12.7)^2 \div 12.7]$

$= 2.0 + 0.5 + 0.5$

$+ 0.78 + 0.05 + 1.17$

$+ 3.53 + 0.13 + 2.21$

$= 10.87$ (calculated value)

However there is one more step before this value can be used.

Degrees of freedom

Calculate the degrees of freedom for your table by multiplying the number of rows minus 1 by the number of columns minus 1.

$$df = (r-1) \times (c-1)$$

With three rows and three columns in the table on page 41, this would mean $df = (3-1) \times (3-1) = 4$. The higher the degrees of freedom value is, the higher the value of the result has to be to be significant.

Check the result

Now we can check whether the differences shown by our Chi-squared value are significant by using a significance table or graph such as the ones below.

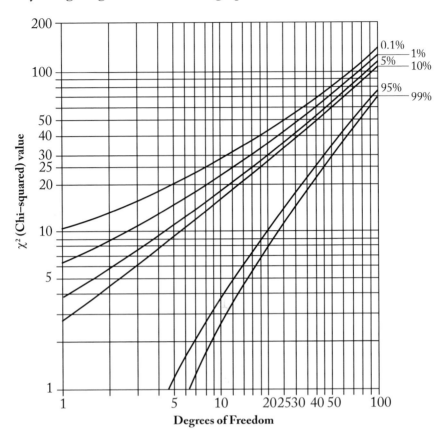

Critical values for Chi–squared test

Degrees of freedom	Significance level 0.05 (95%)	Significance level 0.01 (99%)
1	3.84	6.64
2	5.99	9.21
3	7.82	11.34
4	9.49	13.28
5	11.07	15.09
6	12.59	16.81
7	14.07	18.48
8	15.51	20.09

If the calculated value exceeds the critical value, the null hypothesis is rejected and the hypothesis is accepted: there *is* a significant difference between the data gathered and the chance values. Should it not exceed the critical value the null hypothesis is accepted: a significant difference does not exist.

Our calculated value of 10.87 exceeds the critical value of 9.49 at the 95% significance level (4 degrees of freedom), but not the 99% level, so we can say that our result is significant at the 95% level.

Significance levels

For the difference to be considered significant by geographers, the result must be higher than the critical value at the 0.05 or 95% significance level. What this means is that in less than 5 occasions out of 100 would the result arise because of chance. If the probability were less than 95 percent, it would not be considered high enough to be accepted as significant. If the 0.01 critical value is exceeded the result is even more significant, providing a 99% significance level. In that case such a result would occur in less than 1 out of every 100 tests where there is not a significant difference.

At the end of the test the null hypothesis can be revisited. We can reject ours as the result showed that there *was* a significant difference. In other words the null hypothesis – 'There is no significant difference between particle sizes at various points downstream other than might occur by chance' – can be rejected in favour of the alternative hypothesis **'There *is* a significant difference between particle sizes at various points downstream other than might occur by chance'.**

Take Note

Requirements for a valid Chi-squared text
- The data must be in counted occurrences for a number of categories.
- The total number of observations must be more than 20.
- No more than 20% of expected values should be less than 5.
- No expected value should be less than 1.

Exam Tip

It is possible that you could be required to complete a Chi-squared test in the A2 examination. However a much higher order skill would be the interpretation of a result and so you should be particularly prepared to do this. This requires knowledge of hypotheses and null hypotheses and of degrees of freedom and significance levels.

You could encounter a Chi-squared result in either of your A2 papers, embedded within a question in A2 1 or A2 2 Section A.

3.6 Location Quotient

This statistical technique is used by geographers to measure the degree to which something is concentrated in one place compared to an area as a whole. It measures how much somewhere has more or less than its share of something. It is often used for studying the industrial geography of a region and also for ethnic composition of areas, but it has other uses too.

The formula is $LQ = \dfrac{RI}{RE} \div \dfrac{NI}{NE}$

where: RI = region's numbers of ethnic group or industry or whatever

RE = region's total numbers

NI = whole area's numbers of ethnic group, industrial employment or whatever

NE = whole area's total numbers

This sounds complicated until you work out a few. Let's try a simple one:

Worked Example

A town has 10,000 inhabitants and has 1,000 people working in textiles. One area of the town, with 1,000 inhabitants, has 100 people who work with textiles. The location quotient for this area of the town is 1.0 (work it out for yourself!). This means that there are exactly the number of people working in textiles in that area as you would expect, given the numbers working in textiles in the town as a whole. In other words, the small area has the same concentration as the whole town.

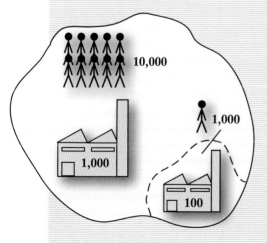

If the numbers working in textiles in the area we are studying were to rise to 200 (but the number working in textiles in the town were to remain at 1,000), the Location Quotient for our area increases to 2.0 – there are twice as many people working in textiles in that area than you would expect, given the concentration in the town as a whole. If we reduce the numbers on our study area to 50 the LQ drops to 0.5 showing a concentration of half that of the town as a whole.

Worked Example

Below is a real example using 2001 Census data (www.nisra.gov.uk)

	Northern Ireland	Ballymena Local Government District	North Down Local Government District
Number of households	626,716	22,059	30,888
Number of households without central heating with sole use of bath/ shower	28,892	1,295	1,121

LQ for Ballymena $= \dfrac{RI}{RE} \div \dfrac{NI}{NE}$

$= \dfrac{1,295}{22,059} \div \dfrac{28,892}{626,716}$

$= 0.0587 \div 0.0461$

$= 1.27$

LQ for North Down $= \dfrac{RI}{RE} \div \dfrac{NI}{NE}$

$= \dfrac{1,121}{30,888} \div \dfrac{28,892}{626,716}$

$= 0.0363 \div 0.0461$

$= 0.79$

This shows that Ballymena Local Government District has a higher concentration of houses without central heating with sole use of bath/shower than would be expected considering Northern Ireland as a whole. Similarly North Down Local Government District has a lower concentration than you would expect, given the concentration in Northern Ireland as whole.

These figures provide precise measures of concentration and allow geographers to start interpretation. What is it about North Down and Ballymena that produces the disparity?

Exam Tip

You should be able to calculate a Location Quotient in the A2 examination and to be able to interpret a table of LQ results. This could occur in either A2 1 or A2 2 Section A.

Preparing for A2

Much of the preparation for your A2 paper will be developing an understanding of the content of the Human Interactions and Global Issues and the Physical Geography parts of the Specification. Learning that content fully, and reflecting on the skills required to answer effectively the questions that will be asked, will form a major part of your preparation.

However, in addition, it is important that you are prepared to answer questions based on the skills that you have developed in data collection and data processing. You should:

- Revise **all** of your statistical techniques, including those from AS (Spearman's rank correlation, nearest neighbour, Chi-squared and Location Quotient)

- Remember the descriptive techniques such as measures of central tendency (mean, mode, median) and spread (range)

- Review the relevant parts of an up-to-date A Level Geography Specification which your teacher will have given you, or which you can access from the CCEA site (www.ccea.org.uk)

- Techniques of data presentation, such as choropleth mapping, scattergraphs and so on should also be covered in preparation for both of your A2 examinations.

4 Graphical Presentation and Mapping Techniques

4.1 Barcharts

A **barchart** or bargraph is one of the simplest and most commonly used methods of geographical representation. Data is displayed in **columns** or **bars** the height of which represents the **quantity** of a discrete component. Each component is measured on the vertical axis using a scale and therefore this method of presentation is useful when comparing quantities eg rainfall values throughout a year.

How to construct a barchart

Precise **title** to explain what the graph shows

y axis scale plotted with accuracy to accommodate highest and lowest values

Label y axis accurately to include units

Label zero value for accuracy

x axis divided into equal sections and labelled to display groups or categories

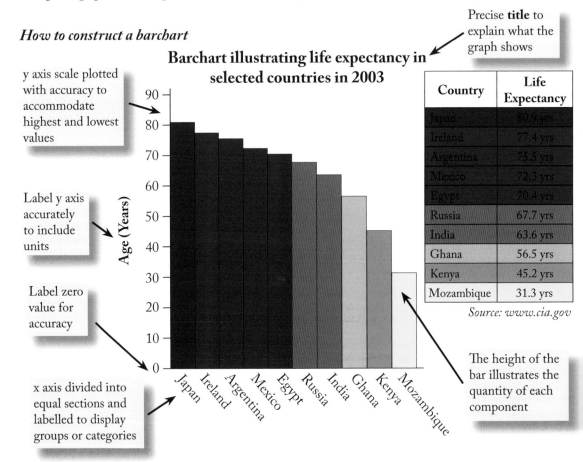

Barchart illustrating life expectancy in selected countries in 2003

Country	Life Expectancy
Japan	80.9 yrs
Ireland	77.4 yrs
Argentina	75.5 yrs
Mexico	72.3 yrs
Egypt	70.4 yrs
Russia	67.7 yrs
India	63.6 yrs
Ghana	56.5 yrs
Kenya	45.2 yrs
Mozambique	31.3 yrs

Source: www.cia.gov

The height of the bar illustrates the quantity of each component

Barchart variations

There are a multitude of variations of the bar chart commonly used to display geographical data. Three examples are shown.

A Reverse Bars

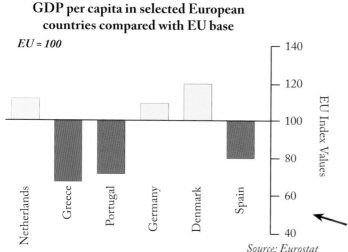

GDP per capita in selected European countries compared with EU base

EU = 100

EU Index Values

Source: Eurostat

Country	GDP per capita EU index value
Spain	80
Denmark	120
Germany	108
Portugal	73
Greece	66
Netherlands	113

This design is an interesting variation which provides a visual comparison of GDP in relation to the EU base line. In this example bars above the base line (EU = 100) illustrate countries which exceed the EU index value. Bars below the base line have GDP values less than the EU index.

B Population Pyramids

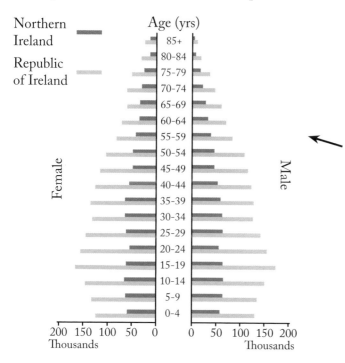

Population Structure - N Ireland & Rep Ireland

Northern Ireland

Republic of Ireland

Age (yrs)

Female

Male

200 150 100 50 0 — 0 50 100 150 200
Thousands — Thousands

Population pyramids, commonly used in demography, are specially designed barcharts which allow geographers to compare age and gender variations in the population.

Source: Statistical & Research Agency and Central Statistics Office

53

C Compound or Component Barcharts

These 'divided' barcharts display the **proportional contribution** of various elements within the total quantity. Components can be displayed as numerical values or as percentages and their relative differences can be visually compared. These bars can be drawn horizontally or vertically.

How to construct a compound barchart

Employment patterns for selected LEDCs and MEDCs				
	Country	Primary Industry (%)	Secondary Industry (%)	Tertiary Industry (%)
LEDCs	Nepal	92	1	7
	Bangladesh	57	10	33
	Mali	85	2	13
MEDCs	UK	3	24	73
	USA	3	21	76
	Germany	4	30	66

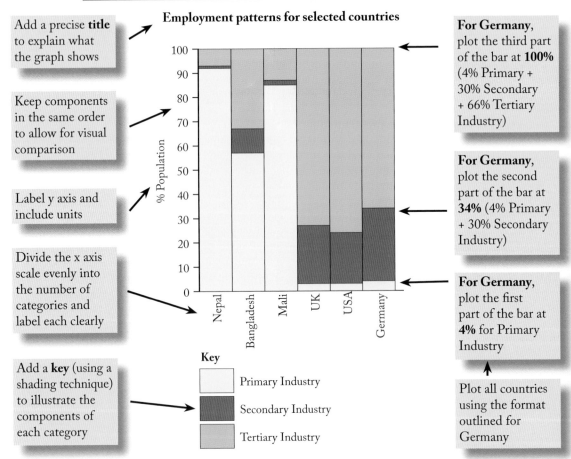

Add a precise **title** to explain what the graph shows

Keep components in the same order to allow for visual comparison

Label y axis and include units

Divide the x axis scale evenly into the number of categories and label each clearly

Add a **key** (using a shading technique) to illustrate the components of each category

Employment patterns for selected countries

For Germany, plot the third part of the bar at **100%** (4% Primary + 30% Secondary + 66% Tertiary Industry)

For Germany, plot the second part of the bar at **34%** (4% Primary + 30% Secondary Industry)

For Germany, plot the first part of the bar at **4%** for Primary Industry

Plot all countries using the format outlined for Germany

Key
- Primary Industry
- Secondary Industry
- Tertiary Industry

4.2 Line Graphs

Line graphs are appropriate when data is continuous. They show how the **dependent** variable (plotted on the y / vertical axis) changes in relation to the **independent** variable (plotted on the x / horizontal axis). They display trends, or changes, which can be absolute or relative. A simple line graph shows how one variable changes, while multiple line graphs show the changes of many variables plotted using the same axes. If the data shows a large range, eg 5 – 50 000, then log or semi-log graph paper will be more suitable.

How to construct a line graph

Population Change in Northern Ireland and Republic of Ireland (1841 – 2001)

Year	Northern Ireland population (thousands)	Republic of Ireland population (thousands)
1841	1649.0	6528.8
1861	1396.4	4402.1
1881	1304.8	3870.0
1901	1237.0	3221.8
1911	1250.5	3139.7
1926	1256.6	2972.0
1946	1313.8	2955.1
1961	1425.0	2818.3
1981	1543.0	3443.4
2001	1689.3	3838.9

Add a specific **title** to explain what the graph shows

Plot and label the **dependent** variable on the y axis. Include units of measurement

Join up points or crosses with a ruler to produce a line

Plot accurately a dot or a cross where the two variables intersect

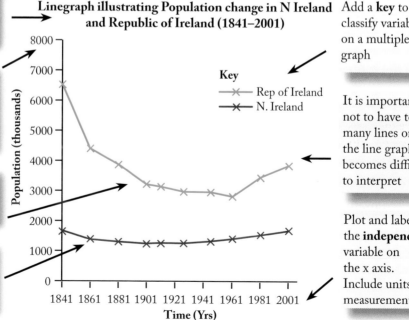

Linegraph illustrating Population change in N Ireland and Republic of Ireland (1841–2001)

Add a **key** to classify variables on a multiple line graph

It is important not to have too many lines or the line graph becomes difficult to interpret

Plot and label the **independent** variable on the x axis. Include units of measurement

Take Note

The data on the x axis is **continuous** ie progression over time, and therefore a line graph is an appropriate graphical presentation technique.

4.3 Piecharts

A **piechart** or piegraph is simply a circle divided into segments which are proportional to the component categories of the data set.

Piecharts are appropriate when the total can be divided into component parts. The circle of the piechart represents 100% and therefore the segments or components should collectively total 100%.

Piecharts can be drawn using raw data or percentages calculated for each component. To construct a piechart it is necessary to calculate the size of each sector in **degrees**. The example shown below illustrates the calculations and method necessary.

Guyana: Ethnic Groups

raw data

To calculate the number of **degrees** divide the population of each ethnic group by the total population and multiply by 360°.

A circle is 360° and therefore the number of degrees is proportional to each segment.

Ethnic Group	Number of people (millions)	Size of piechart segment (degrees)
East Indian	29.8	183.6
African	16.94	104.4
Mixed	8.19	50.4
Amerindian	2.4	14.4
European/Chinese	1.17	7.2
Total	58.5	360°

Example: The number of degrees for the European/Chinese sector

$$= \frac{1.17}{58.5} \times \frac{360}{1} = 7.2^o$$

Take Note

If values are recorded as percentages, then multiply by **3.6** to obtain the number of degrees for each sector. A circle is 360° and each percent is one hundredth of the circle.

Therefore 1% is equal to:-

360 ÷ 100 = 3.6^O

How to construct a Piechart

Radial line used to begin plotting the first sector

Title to explain what piechart shows

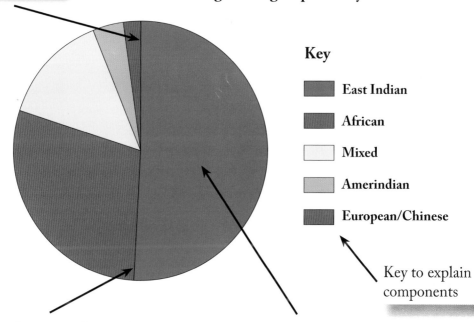

Piechart illustrating ethnic groups in Guyana

Key

East Indian

African

Mixed

Amerindian

European/Chinese

Key to explain components

Plot the first sector by measuring 183.6^O using a protractor and drawing the radius

It is advisable to start with the largest category and then work clockwise around the circle in descending order of size

4.4 Proportional graphs

Proportional graphs use the area of the symbols to represent the sizes of a variable eg unemployment rates. The most common shapes used include circles, squares and triangles. A square which is twice the height and twice the width of another square will represent **four** times the value of the other. Often circles are used in proportional graphs with the area of the circle proportional to what is being shown. For example, Scottish visitors to Northern Ireland spent 12 times more than Welsh visitors in 2001 (£48 million compared to £4 million). If these figures were being drawn on a proportional circle then the **area** of the Scottish circle should be 12 times greater than the Welsh one.

Sometimes these circles are placed on a map to provided *located* proportional circles. Often these circles are divided, so that for example visitors of different nationalities are represented within the proportional pie charts showing different visitor numbers. While this can be an effective graphical technique, it is often difficult for the viewer to distinguish the difference between the numbers represented in a small segment of a large 'pie' and those in a large segment of a small 'pie'.

Source of tourists in Northern Ireland 1972, 1986 and 2001

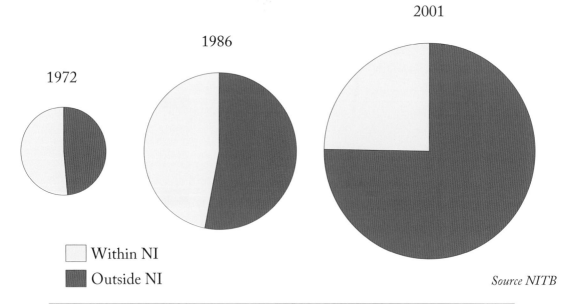

Within NI

Outside NI

Source NITB

Year	From outside NI	From within NI	Total
1972	435,000	457,000	892.000
1986	824,100	727,600	1,551,700
2001	1,676,000	548,000	2,224,000

Care should be taken when interpreting proportional graphs as they can also be extended into 3-D symbols such as spheres or cubes. In this case the volume of the symbol is what represents the values shown on the graph. Thus a cube which is twice the width, height and length represents eight times the value of the other cube. Occasionally the graph may use a symbol such as a bag of grain to represent the data. The viewer has to be clear whether the data are being drawn on a volume or an area basis. Sometimes a close examination of these graphs, even from reputable sources, betrays a lack of understanding by those who have produced the graph – a good reason for using a trained cartographer to draw maps and graphs!

Numbers of visitors to selected NI tourist attractions (2001)

Attraction	Number of visitors
Giant's Causeway Visitor Centre	383,133
W5	200,893
Castle Espie Wildfowl and Wetland Centre	64,600
Portrush Countryside Centre	49,500

Source NITB

Exam Tip

Constructing a graph of this sort is time consuming and it is unlikely that you will be asked to do this during any of your A Level Examinations. However, you must know and understand this type of graph and be able to analyse it. A graph of this sort could form part of the resources in any of your A Level examination papers.

4.5 *Mapping Techniques:* **Triangular graphs**

Key Features

Triangular, or ternary, graphs can be used for data representation when **three** component variables collectively comprise a total of 100%. Each proportional component is plotted on the axis of an equilateral triangle. The three variables, when plotted, form one single point on the triangular graph. The relative value of each of the component variables influences the location of the plot on the triangular graph.

Take Note

Triangular graphs have limited applicability due to their key features but are frequently used in human geography to display age structure and employment structure data. In physical geography they are commonly used to display soil textural composition (component percentages of sand, silt and clay).

Exam Tip

Careful attention is required when constructing and analysing a triangular graph. Distinct clusterings of values on the triangular graph may emerge revealing a quick visual comparison of the differences within the data set, which can aid geographical interpretation.

How to construct a Triangular graph

- Angle x = 60°.
- Each axis displays values ranging from 0 to 100%, usually with guidelines indicating each 10%.
- Each component is plotted using axes as illustrated on the equilateral triangle.
- The plotting of each of the three components results in one single plot value.
- **Note:** all three components collectively comprise 100%.

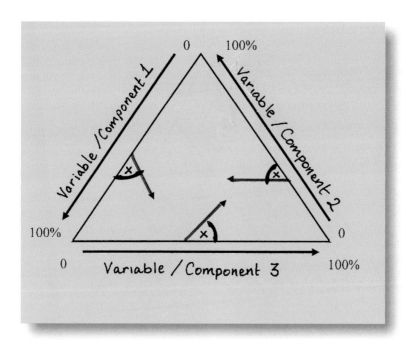

Triangular Graph illustrating Age Structure data for 10 selected countries

Country	Percentage Population 0–14.9 years	Percentage Population 15–64.9 years	Percentage Population 65+ years
1. Angola	43.7	53.5	2.8
2. Ethiopia	43.4	53.8	2.7
3. Mali	48.2	48.8	3.1
4. Burkino Faso	46.7	50.9	2.5
5. Sierra Leone	44.8	52.0	3.2
6. Canada	17.3	69.2	13.5
7. France	18.6	65.2	16.2
8. UK	17.2	67.0	15.8
9. Austria	15.1	67.5	17.5
10. Germany	13.9	66.3	19.8

www.cia.gov

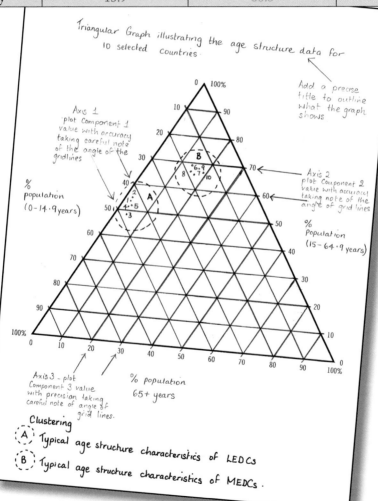

4.6 *Mapping Techniques:* **Scattergraphs**

Scattergraphs are used to graphically present two sets of data when a potential relationship requires investigation.

How to construct a scattergraph

- Plot the independent variable on the horizontal axis and the dependant variable on the vertical axis.

- Use each pair of values to plot each point where intersection occurs on the graph paper.

- If a positive or negative trend emerges (pages 28 and 29) this can be visually displayed using a line of best fit. A mathematical process known as linear regression can be employed to plot this line with precision, although this is not an essential requirement at AS level. It can be subjectively drawn using a ruler to clarify the trend. An effort should be made to represent the linear trend of values with approximately an equal number of points on either side of the line.

- The closer the points are to the trend line the greater the degree of correlation. Points which lie some distance from the trend line can be recognised as residual values.

- Scattergraph can be plotted on arithmetic, logarithmic or semi-logarithmic graph paper. This will depend on the range of values within the data set.

Take Note

Although a visual trend on a scattergraph may appear to provide evidence of a relationship, it is essential to use statistical analysis (Spearman's Rank Correlation) to determine the reliability of the conclusion. This statistical technique allows the researcher to establish if, or to what extent, the relationship may have occurred by chance. Geographers require significance either to accept or reject a hypothesis in order to produce valid, reliable conclusions.

Scattergraph illustrating the relationship between Wealth (PPP) and Life Expectancy for 12 selected countries

	Country	Wealth (People Purchasing Parity– US$)	Life Expectancy (years)
MEDCs	1. Canada	33,375	80.3
	2. Spain	27,169	80.5
	3. Japan	31,267	85.9
	4. Italy	28,529	80.3
	5. UK	33,238	79.0
	6. France	30,386	80.2
LEDCs	7. Senegal	1,792	62.3
	8. Angola	2,335	41.7
	9. Pakistan	2,370	64.6
	10. Peru	6,039	70.7
	11. Colombia	7,304	72.3
	12. Brazil	8,402	71.7

Human Development Report Office

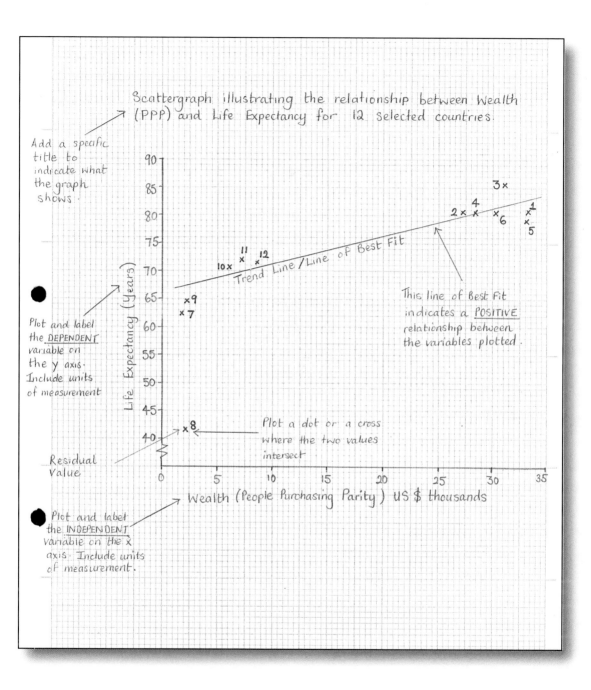

Scattergraph illustrating the relationship between Wealth (PPP) and Life Expectancy for 12 selected countries.

Add a specific title to indicate what the graph shows

Plot and label the DEPENDENT variable on the y axis. Include units of measurement

Residual Value

Plot and label the INDEPENDENT variable on the x axis. Include units of measurement.

Life Expectancy (Years)

Trend Line / Line of Best Fit

This line of Best Fit indicates a POSITIVE relationship between the variables plotted.

Plot a dot or a cross where the two values intersect

Wealth (People Purchasing Parity) US $ thousands

4.7 *Mapping Techniques:* Choropleth maps

A choropleth map is one which is shaded to show the relative **density** of an area. The gradation of colour reflects the range of values and the deepest most intense colour illustrates the highest values. The shading indicates visually contrasting distribution patterns between regions. Although relatively easy to interpret, constructing a choropleth map can be much more challenging.

How to construct a choropleth map

Choropleth map illustrating car ownership throughout the standard regions of the UK

Region of UK	Households with 1+ cars (%)
North East	58
North West	69
Y & H'side	66
E Midlands	73
W Midlands	68
East	77
London	61
South East	81
South West	76
Wales	69
Scotland	65
N Ireland	70

Specific **title** to explain what the map shows

Shading: Gradation of tone with the deepest colours showing **highest** values and lightest colours showing **lowest** values

Label categories and state units in the key

Class Boundaries These should not overlap or leave gaps and should cover the range of values in the table

Key: Households with one or more car (%)

☐ Less than 60
☐ 60 – 69.9
☐ 70 – 79.9
■ 80 and over
— Standard region boundary

Map is completed using the shading outlined in the key

Choropleth maps are a useful way to display variations in social and economic indicators

N

Scotland

Northern Ireland

North East

North West

Yorkshire and Humberside

East Midlands

West Midlands

East

Wales

London

South East

South West

0   150
km

To produce a choropleth map, cartographers (map drawers) need to:

- **Devise suitable classes.** The data must be grouped into classes or categories. It is important to consider the number of classes necessary to cover the entire range of values present. Four to six groups is often quoted as desirable. Suitable class boundaries need to be established but class intervals do not need to be uniform. It is important that boundary values do not overlap and it is equally important to ensure that gaps do not occur between classes.

- **Consider appropriate shading.** Shading should be graded from dark to light. Darkest tones indicate highest values while lightest tones show lowest values. This can be very effective visually when varying tones of one colour are used.

An alternative method of shading

| Darkest tone | | Lightest tone |
| Highest value | **Gradation of tone** | Lowest value |

Take Note
Limitations of choropleth mapping

Although choropleth maps provide geographers with a striking visual image of contrasting distribution patterns, it is important to recognise that:

- Oversimplification will have occurred. They present an area or region as having a uniform value range and therefore fail to present possible intra-regional variations.

- Maps often provide striking contrasts at regional boundary zones, which can be unrealistic.

4.8 *Mapping Techniques:* Dot distribution maps

A dot map is an effective and relatively simple mapping technique used to display a geographical **distribution**.

Each dot represents a specific value and their distribution and density on a map allow a geographer to interpret patterns.

Dots can be distributed randomly within defined 'regions' or alternatively they can be plotted in actual locations if the information is available.

Brazilian State	% area deforested
Amapa	2
Para	13
Maranhao	35
Tocatins	9
Mato Grosso	11
Rondonia	14
Acre	7
Amazonas	2
Roraima	2

Precise **title** to explain what the map shows

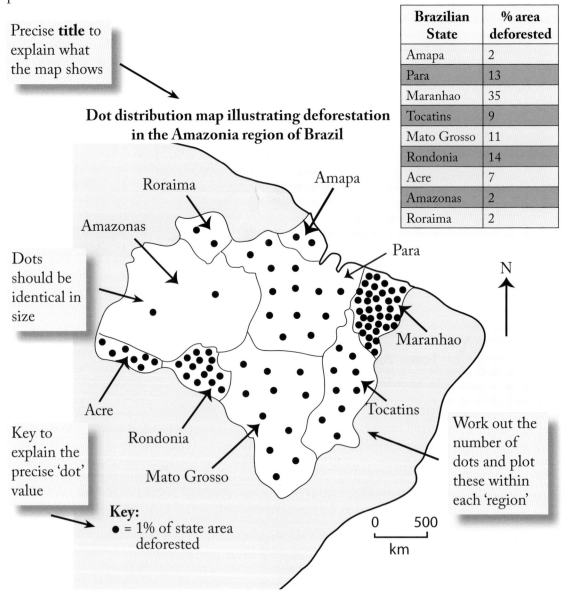

Dot distribution map illustrating deforestation in the Amazonia region of Brazil

Dots should be identical in size

Key to explain the precise 'dot' value

Work out the number of dots and plot these within each 'region'

Key:
● = 1% of state area deforested

0   500
km

4.9 *Mapping Techniques:* **Flow line maps**

Flow lines are drawn to display visually the **volume** and **direction** of movement between two defined locations.

The **width of the line** is proportional to the quantity of movement, and the **arrow** indicates the direction of flow. They can be used effectively to represent a wide range of geographical information including traffic, migration and tourist flows.

How to construct a flow line chart

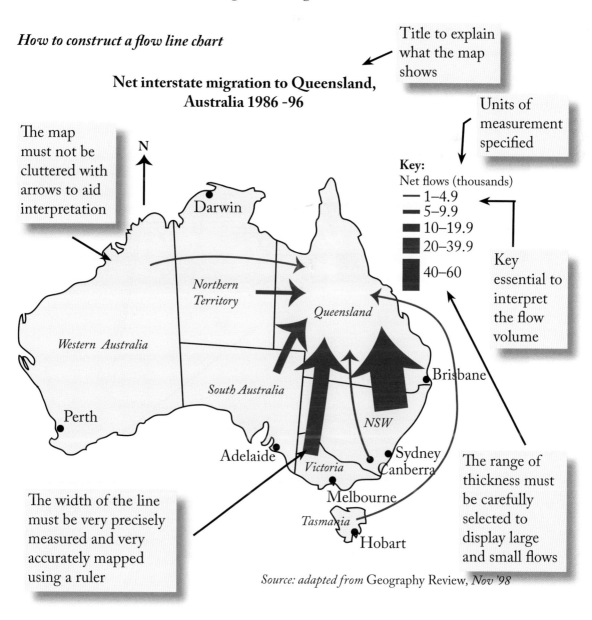

Title to explain what the map shows

Net interstate migration to Queensland, Australia 1986 -96

Units of measurement specified

The map must not be cluttered with arrows to aid interpretation

N

Key:
Net flows (thousands)
— 1–4.9
— 5–9.9
10–19.9
20–39.9
40–60

Key essential to interpret the flow volume

Darwin

Northern Territory

Queensland

Western Australia

South Australia

Brisbane

Perth

NSW

Adelaide

Sydney
Canberra

Victoria

Melbourne

The range of thickness must be carefully selected to display large and small flows

The width of the line must be very precisely measured and very accurately mapped using a ruler

Tasmania

Hobart

Source: adapted from Geography Review, *Nov '98*

4.10 *Mapping Techniques:* **Annotated sketch maps**

The sketch maps here used the 1:50,000 map accompanying the White Strand golf course Decision Making Exercise (Module 5: 2001).

A sketch map emphasising physical features

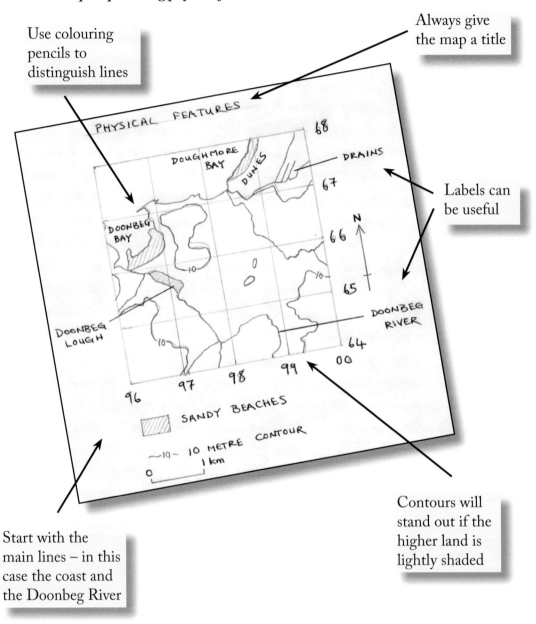

Always give the map a title

Use colouring pencils to distinguish lines

Labels can be useful

Start with the main lines – in this case the coast and the Doonbeg River

Contours will stand out if the higher land is lightly shaded

A sketch map emphasising human features

Only add the
detail that you
are required to

Draw the grid
lines lightly to
act as guides

Number the
grid lines

Add a key if
necessary

Add a scale and
a north sign

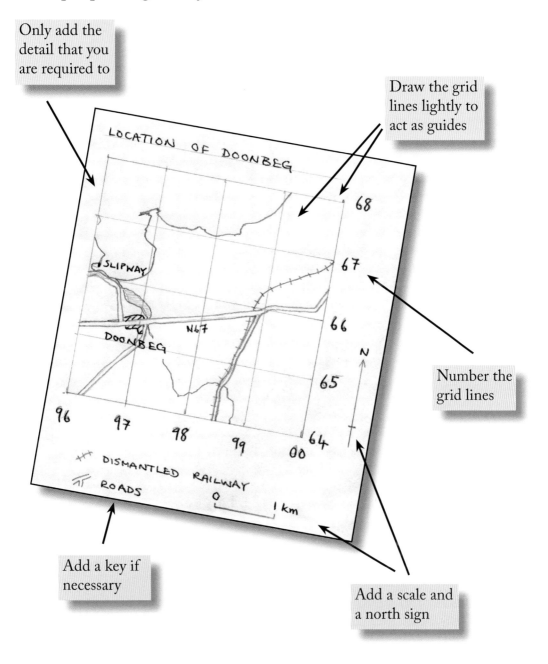

4.11 *Mapping Techniques:* Isoline maps

Isolines are lines which join together points of the same value. Examples are:

- isotherms, joining places of the same temperature together
- isobars, joining places of the same air pressure together
- isohyets, joining places with the same rainfall together
- contours, joining places with the same height above sea level together

Diagram A

The interpolation between points

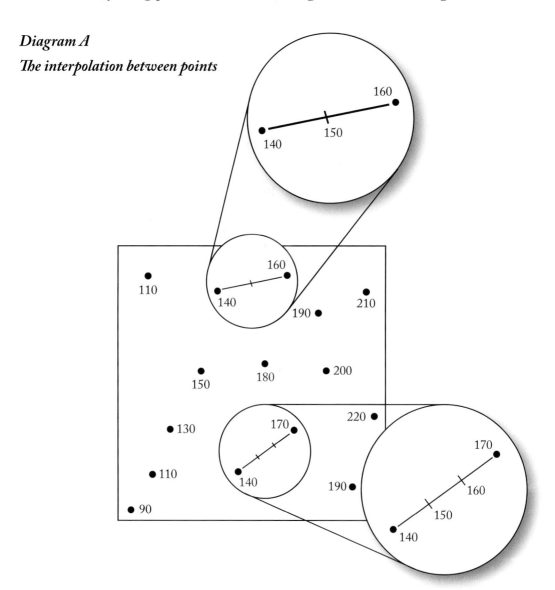

Mapping isolines involves interpolation (meaning *between two points*). A meteorologist may know the annual rainfall in Point A is 1150 mm and at Point B is 850 mm. He can then interpolate the value of 1000 mm exactly half way between them. When a number of such values are known the points can be joined to give isohyets (see diagrams A and B).

In interpolation the assumption is made that the change between two points is steady, and it may not be. Nevertheless we can be sure that there **must** be a 1000 millibar value between a point with 980 Mb and another with 1010 Mb but it may not always lie exactly two thirds of the way between these points. However any inaccuracies so produced will generally be small and the more points used to create an isoline map the more accurate the result will be.

Diagram B

The interpolation

joined up

Exam Tip

Constructing isoline maps by interpolation is time consuming so it is unlikely that you will be required to do much of this in any of your A Level examinations. However you must be familiar with the technique and its purpose. Additionally, you should be able to interpret an isoline map, whether using isohyets, contours, isotherms or any other isolines. You could come across these in any of the resources in any of your A Level examination papers.

5 Decision Making

The Decision Making Exercise (DME) in A Level Geography has changed little since it was first introduced in 1988. You will be presented with a variety of resources related to a real-world contemporary geographical issue. Recent issues have included an expansion of the canal in Panama (2008), the proposed building of the Thames Gateway Bridge, London (2007), a gas pipeline and terminal in Mayo (2006), a hydroelectric plant in Iceland (2005) and a waste incinerator in County Meath (2004). In each case the candidates needed to use their geographical skills to examine conflicting viewpoints about the issue. They were required to take on a rôle, usually that of a planner or government minister, and using their geographical skills had to set the issue in context and describe the implications of each position. Finally a decision was made in relation to the proposed development and was justified.

The types of resources used are unlikely to change much from year to year. There will be a question, Question 7, in Section B of the Physical Geography and Decision Making Paper, and a series of resources such as text, maps, tables and photographs in the Resource Booklet. There may sometimes be a separate map.

5.1 Written resources

There will be a number of written resources. One may give a background to the issue and there may be information from the main parties with an interest in the proposed development. A context for the issue is provided in the question paper and this often contains information which should be used. Generally there are a number of quotations summarising the views of some of the parties involved.

Maps

There are usually a range of maps showing the location of the development and more detailed maps showing the development in more detail. There is often a separate Ordnance Survey map, generally 1:50,000 but sometimes 1:25,000. These maps always have a key attached so there is no requirement to learn all the symbols associated with these maps.

Photographs

These are also often included in Decision Making Exercises and can be useful to help you to form a picture of the area. Occasionally there are photographs of models of the proposed development or artist's impressions showing what the development may look like if it were to go ahead. It is often possible to refer to these photographs, such as the one below, in your answer. This photograph shows a sign reflecting the beliefs of those opposed to a waste incinerator in County Meath and comments in your answer could relate to the sign, to the road traffic or to the landscape of the area.

Graphs or diagrams

These are sometimes used to illustrate complex data related to the issue and are likely to be important sources of information for your answer. The graph below, for example, appeared on the 2002 paper about a proposed fifth terminal for Heathrow Airport. It shows the loudness of individual noise events at Hounslow, near to the airport. The graph could have been used to back up the case of those opposing another terminal as loud noises begin to be commonplace at 4.30 am. Equally, loud noises could be argued to be relatively infrequent between 11.00 pm and 6.00 am and this could have been used in evidence by those in favour of the new terminal. This graph was an important resource in the arguments in relation to Terminal 5.

Source: Dept of Transport (1993) Report of the Field Study of Aircraft Noise and Sleep Disturbance

Tables

There are often one or more tables of data which you may be required to redraw as a graph and incorporate into the report.

Not all issues will require all of these resources, but most will be present each year. Do not neglect any of the resources. All resources included in the DME should allow you to support or to counter some point of view or to provide a context for the issue. This is particularly true of photographs and other illustrations which you should refer to if you can.

This should be an easy two marks – make your headings and sub-headings clear

Adopt the role and maintain it but do not overdo it – it is worth two marks only

For the purpose of this exercise you are required to assume the role of a Planner for An Bord Pleanála.

	Marks	
Format	2	Each of the three sections must be clearly set out with heading and sub–headings as required
Role	2	You must adopt and maintain the stated role
Graph	8	Draw a graph using all the data from **Table A, Resource B** and incorporate it into the report at an appropriate place

Make sure you use the correct data to draw your graph

Ensure that you refer to the graph in your report

Heading	Sub–heading	Sub-section	Section	Guidance to candidates
The report must be structured as below		Marks		
A Introduction		8	8	A Briefly describe the proposed development and explain its potential importance to the Republic of Ireland
B The likely impact of the Corrib Natural Gas Project on	i) The local environment	10		B i) Discuss the possible negative impact on the environment and the responses of those in favour of the development
	ii) The local economy	10	20	ii) Discuss how the proposed development would affect the local economy, both positively and negatively.
C Decision		10	10	C State clearly your decision and justify it on the basis of the greater overall benefits.

Command words like these are very important. Know the difference between them

Note that you have to give both sides – try to have a balance in detail and length

This is where the bulk of the marks are to be earned. You should time your answer accordingly

This is your opportunity to argue for your decision **and** to argue why the other decision is not as valid

An example of a question from a Decision Making Exercise

5.2 Structure

The **structure** of the Decision Making Exercise will also remain little changed from year to year with an introduction, a section on the impact of the development and a conclusion.

Introduction

You are required to introduce the issue. It is important that you follow the wording of the question here as it is likely that there will be specific aspects of the issue that are required for the introduction. It may be that you will have to use a number of resources to find out about the issue and to address the question. The introduction may ask you to set the proposed development in a context. Sometimes this is a national context – in other words you might have to explain the importance of the development for the *country* in which it is to be built. In that case you must look for those resources that indicate the impact on the country as a whole and use those in your answer. In other cases they may be looking for a regional context and in that case you have to find different resources. The introduction may not be looking at the importance of the issue at all but may, for example, want a description of how it has arisen. The key here, as elsewhere, is to read carefully the requirements of the introduction in the question paper and to spend some time making sure that you are clear about what is required.

Impact of the development

Typically this section is worth the most marks and, if so, you should spend most time on it. It will be divided up for you into subsections. These will vary according to the issue being addressed but are likely to cover a couple of the potential consequences of the proposed development. These might be economic, social or environmental and you will probably be required to look at the benefits and drawbacks of the consequences highlighted. It is worth reminding ourselves of what we might have to consider in each of these.

Economic

Will the development bring jobs to the area, increase the earnings and the wealth of the area? Will it cause job losses elsewhere? Will there be a cost in other forms of economic activity?

A quarry, for example, will bring more jobs to an area but might also cause a reduction in jobs in tourism, if it is unsightly or polluting.

Social

Will the proposed development have a positive impact on the people in the area, other than providing them with jobs (an economic benefit)? Will it provide them with more facilities? Will it improve the infrastructure – roads, schools, power supplies, and so on? Will it encourage people to remain in the area and will it improve the quality of life? On the other hand it could have a negative social impact on people if it were to go ahead.

Environmental

Will the development have an impact on the natural environment? This might be pollution of some form (visual, water, air for example) or threats to habitats of native plants and animals. Many proposed developments will claim that they are protecting or even improving the environment or at least minimising the negative impact that they might have.

It is likely that you will be asked to look at the benefits and the drawbacks of the proposed development going ahead. Sometimes you are required to look at the arguments for and the arguments against the proposal. For example, you might have to discuss the pollution which it is claimed the development will cause and then look at the arguments that claim that the pollution threat is unfounded.

Each Decision Making Exercise will be different in its requirements, depending on the actual issue. In some issues the focus may be on the environmental and economic impact, and on others the social and the environmental may form the components examined, for example. In some cases an aspect of the potential impact may be so great that the question is divided into two sections – for example the environment may be divided into noise pollution and visual pollution. However there are likely to be two main sections here although you should look very carefully at the requirements of the sub-sections to ensure that you are answering the question fully.

Do remember that you are given **all** the information that you need to provide each answer – you only have to bring with you 'critical understanding'. The knack is to select efficiently all of the relevant facts that you require in each section (some candidates favour the use of different coloured highlighters to help in this task) and to demonstrate an understanding of the information in your presentation of it. As you cannot just repeat the original text, you often have to reconstruct the information provided in a different form, while retaining the sense of the original. This means that you need to develop an understanding of the issue as rapidly as possible. Practice using past papers is often the best way of doing this, but do remember that the question details will differ from issue to issue, and any changes to the Specification since the past paper was taken will have to be taken into account.

Conclusion

In this section you are normally required to state your decision and to justify it on the basis of 'the greater overall benefits'. This could be a repeat of the previous section if you are not careful. Do not go over the ground you have covered before. Instead this is an opportunity to compare the arguments and to weigh them up against each other. You could start your justification with "The development company claim that 250 jobs will be created in this development. However local people point out that few of those will be available to them and those that are will be low paid." Alternatively you could argue "While local people fear that few of the jobs created in the development will be available to them, the development company have stated that there will be 250 jobs in all and this will give a considerable boost to the local economy". While these examples lack the detail that you could provide in a real situation, they do show one argument being set against another, which is exactly what is required in this section.

Other aspects of structure

Rôle – you are generally provided with 1 or 2 marks for this and the question will require you to 'adopt and maintain' a rôle. A glance at a Mark Scheme for past papers will show that a candidate will be awarded one mark when they *adopt* the rôle on the first occasion ("As Secretary of State, I …") and a second mark, where available, for the second occasion in a different section when they *maintain* the rôle. Do not write a long covering letter as that wastes valuable time and may earn only 1 mark. Also make clear that it is you playing the rôle, rather than you as a candidate who is writing. "I do not want the development to go ahead because …" will *not* be considered to be adopting the rôle.

Format – you are rewarded if you follow the instructions for this, usually by using clearly the headings and sub-headings provided. Do this by using the wording of the headings and sub-headings as provided and lay these out clearly so that they stand out from the body text. You could underline them, or put them in upper case, and put them on a separate line from the rest of your answer. Also, leave a space between each section.

Graph or other skill – at some stage you are required to demonstrate a geographical skill. This is generally drawing a graph using data provided.

5.3 Techniques

Timing

Good timing is essential in this, as in any other examination. However it is a particular challenge in a paper which combines a DME with other questions. You should look at the allocation of marks within the question and divide your time accordingly. Very often markers of A level papers comment on candidates penalising themselves by omitting sections of the paper through poor timing. In a DME this is sometimes the graph being left out because of time constraints. Sometimes too little time is left to do justice to an important part of the question. Often examiners can spot a candidate who is likely to suffer from time problems later in the paper if they have written unnecessarily long answers to questions early in the paper.

Pay attention to the mark allocation within questions. You should have familiarised yourself with the structure of the paper beforehand, using a past paper appropriate to this Specification. You should make a calculation of timing before you start, using the instructions on the front cover of the paper to help you. You can do this in advance, following the recommendations in the Information for Candidates section on the front cover of your examination paper. For parts of questions within each section, you should make a calculation before you begin each section. Check these calculations very carefully as an error here could be very costly.

WARNING FROM THE CHIEF EXAMINER: NOT COMPLETING ALL PARTS OF YOUR EXAMINATION PAPER WILL COST MARKS!

CCEA, in their Information for Candidates on the cover of the examination paper, strongly recommend that you spend one hour answering the two questions from the two optional Physical Geography units that you have studied. Ignore this advice at your peril. If you have managed your time well, there will remain 1 hour and 30 minutes for the Decision Making exercise. Attempting the DME with less time than this may prove difficult. You are also advised on the Examination cover to spend 30 minutes reading the resources and selecting those you plan to use in your answer. This should leave 60 minutes for the answer itself. The DME is worth 50 marks which equates to about 1 minute per mark, with a little leeway. If, for example, a question is allocated 8 marks, you should spend about 8 minutes answering it. If you can answer it effectively in less time, then that is a bonus. However, it is most unlikely that you could provide an effective answer in 4 minutes. Another mistake would be to spend 14 minutes. That would be likely to put you into time problems later on and, in any case, spending 14 minutes is unlikely to gain you more marks.

The graph, if it is required, means that you have to select a suitable graphical technique – a line graph, bar graph or whatever – and use it to represent some data provided in the paper. This is typically allocated 7 or 8 marks. However it is possible that this will take a little longer than 7 or 8 minutes to complete so a small amount of additional time has to be allowed for this – probably some of the additional 10 minutes leeway discussed earlier. It is a serious mistake to omit this or other parts of the task as this will impact on your marks and could cost a grade or more.

Skills

The skills section of the DME has most often required you to show that you can represent in a graph some information provided in a table in the resource booklet. You know a number of graph types including proportional, line, bar and pie.

Only use a line graph when time or some other continuous measurement is along one axis. For data when figures are in separate categories, a bar graph is usually more appropriate. Only in Table a, below, would a line graph be appropriate.

Table a: Revenue from Tourism in Northern Ireland (£million)

1997	268
1998	280
1999	322
2000	329
2001	348

Table b: Distance travelled to shop (kms)

0–10.9	147
11–25.9	23
26–50	6

Table c: Land use in a town (%)

Residential	58
Industrial	10
Retail	21
Derelict	8
Vacant	3

Think carefully before you select the type of graph that you are using to ensure it is the appropriate technique.

Pie charts and proportional graphs are very effective ways of showing information but will probably take too long to construct in the short time available in the examination, so it is likely that your graph will be a bar graph or line graph.

Correct placement of the diagram within the appropriate section is often rewarded as is making reference to the diagram in the body of your answer ("As the graph below shows …") If you feel that it would interrupt the flow of your answer to stop and draw the diagram, then leave a space and return to it later. Do ensure that you leave enough time to do this.

Many marks are lost by not having the usual conventions on a graph. Use something like the following mnemonic and checklist to ensure that you have not left anything out.

T I have given the graph a correct **title** ☐

R I have made a **reference** to the graph in the body of my answer ☐

A I have labelled the **vertical axis** fully (including units eg tonnes) ☐

A I have labelled the **horizontal axis** fully (including units eg years) ☐

K I have drawn a correct **key**, where necessary ☐

Decision

As you worked your way through the materials in the Decision Making Exercise, you may have determined which decision you are going to make ultimately, when you come to the conclusion of your answer. Most people suggest that you should make up your mind very early on what your decision is to be. If you have decided early on in the process, you can be marshalling your arguments for the conclusion as you sift through the material for other sections. You can also retain material which is more appropriate for the conclusion and not have gone into the intricacies of them in the impact section.

Mind mapping

Some people are helped in their visualisation of an issue by drawing a mind map which can help to tease out the aspects of the issue. If you are using this technique in an examination be careful not to make it too detailed as that might pose time difficulties. All examiners have come across candidates who have spent much too long on a plan of their answer, only to fail to complete the answer itself.

The diagram overleaf gives an example of a mind map that might have been drawn by a

Mind map for Corrib Gas Pipeline and terminal

Describe proposed development
- Corrib gas discovered 1996 Background 1
- 83km Background 1
- 1.7 M cubic ms pa for 15–20 yrs Background 1
- Dooncarton B1

Terminal details B3

Potential importance to RoI
- Essential for economy B6
- 80% imported B6
- Vulnerable B7/8
- Refer to Graph A

Introduction

Graph here

Decision

Against
- Visual impact F7/F8 tied to tourism F9
- Removed peat and dangers F4
- Short term advantage long term disadvantage F9
- Need for longer term development – 20 years short time
- Local people don't want H2 H4
- Jobs fisheries/tourism F3/F9 vs proposal G3

Corrib Gas Pipeline and terminal

Keep it national!

Just 8 marks

Role – Two places!!!

LIKELY IMPACT

Local **environment**

Possible negative impact
- Stability in peat F2
- Inshore fishermen – shellfish and finfish F3
- Peat that is moved F4
- Landslides F4
- Visual pollution F7/F8
- 40 m flare tower F8

Responses of those in favour
- No impact on tourism G4
- Screening by existing conifers G8
- Poor land G8
- Treatment of waste water G9
- Traffic impact – short, small, localised G4

Use OS Map detail

Local **economy** (positive)
- Need for employment G1
- Population decline G1
- Deprivation G1
- Income 400 local 700 construction G3
- 2 million euros G3
- 100 full time jobs + indirect G3
- Local people want – quote Gerry Coyle H1

Local **economy** (negative)
- Reduce tourism F9
- Tourists value scenery and wild, unspoiled landscape – both threatened F9
- Short term economic benefit – long term economic damage F9
- Fishing industry 90 jobs F3
- Few benefits locally F6
- Don't need gas now F5

candidate who was against the proposed development of the gas pipeline and terminal in County Mayo, on the specimen paper provided with the Specification. The structure of the diagram is based on the question and the mind map could be used both to summarise the relevant information, and to provide a plan for answering the question. This diagram has been written so that someone else can make sense of it – a real one is likely to use more abbreviations and other devices to save time. In this case the candidate has produced the mind map structure during the 30 minutes prior to answering the question. While going through the resource booklet information, points have been noted on the mind map. He or she has numbered the paragraphs in the resource booklet and gives letters and paragraph numbers on the plan to allow easy retrieval of information from the resource booklet when the answer is started.

If you were to use this technique, remember that it is only for use by you. It is not a problem if only you can decipher some of the abbreviations on it for example. If you find this technique too time consuming (and you should practice it using past papers to find out if it helps you), then find another way of visualising the issue, summarising the main points and planning your answer. While the mind map, or other technique, is for you, an examiner may give some credit for the 'plan', if there is some difficulty with time.

Levels of response mark schemes

It is important to know how your questions are being marked so that you can answer in a way that will make your work 'score' as much as possible. All longer questions are marked using Levels. There are usually three of these and the details of them for each question are provided each year in the detailed mark scheme for the paper that your teacher will have. A typical version is shown overleaf.

You do not have to write more to get to Level 3; you just have to show a clearer understanding of the points

Make sure that you do not bring in material that is not relevant to that section

Level 3 (11-15)

Candidate states clearly the main argument and the counter-argument. Two or more factors should be discussed. The points made will be consistently relevant and logically structured and show an insight into the issue. Most of the relevant resource material will be used and no significant points will be omitted. Figures where available and appropriate will be used effectively.

If arguing two sides to an issue, try to make sure they balance in length and detail

There is no requirement to use all of the resources, but most will have a role to play in your answer

Level 2 (6-10)

Fewer lines of discussion but, while ideas may lack detail or depth, they are still adequate. There may be a heavy imbalance between the two sides of the argument and there may be an over-reliance on direct quotes from the resources. Some of the resources will not be as well used as they might be and some irrelevant material may be introduced.

Do not copy out the resources – make sure you put the arguments in your own words

Do not use words like 'a lot of' or 'few' if you can use figures from the resources instead

Level 1 (1-5)

Simple understanding is shown but the argument is sketchily dealt with. The resource material is used but many relevant resources are omitted and there is little structure or logic in the ordering of content.

You need to use the detail in the resources to show your understanding of the issue

Making a plan or mind map is essential

When you are able to distinguish between a Level 2 and a Level 3 answer, for example, you are much closer to being able to provide a Level 3 response yourself. You should practice marking parts of your own and others' answers, allocating them to levels and giving them a mark within those levels.

Exam Tip

You might imagine that you cannot prepare in advance for an unseen decision making examination. For example you do not know whether the decision is to be about a harbour development in Germany or a road widening scheme in Scotland.

It is true that you do not know the issue with which you will be faced nor its location. You do not know the full details of the task you have to do or the rôle that you will be asked to adopt.

Nevertheless there is **a lot** you can do in advance of the examination.

- Review the Decision Making Exercises you have done with your teacher, including past papers where available.

- Revise the data presentation skills and the checklist for graph conventions.

- Examine the front cover of a recent Decision Making Exercise, appropriate to this Specification, to become familiar with the details in the Instructions to Candidates and Information for Candidates, including the advice on timings. You will still have to do this in the Examination Hall but prior thought should reduce the likelihood of a mistake being made.

- Reflect on the levels of response mark scheme – how can you maximise your marks?

- Remind yourself how important good timing is and also how vital it is not to omit any part of the examination paper.

Resources for **CCEA** **A Level Geography**
from Colourpoint Educational

Find out more at **www.colourpointeducational.com** or contact us on:
T: 028 9182 0505   F: 028 9182 1900   E: sales@colourpoint.co.uk

Colourpoint
Educational

Geography for CCEA AS Level
Martin Thom and Eileen Armstrong

TITLE	Geography for CCEA AS Level	PRICE	£25
ISBN	978 1 904242 90 1	PAGES	200pp
TITLE	Resource CD	PRICE	£39.99 + VAT
ISBN	978 1 904242 79 6	CONTENTS	Diagrams in jpeg format

Geography for CCEA A2 Level
Martin Thom and Eileen Armstrong

TITLE	Geography for CCEA A2 Level	PRICE	£28
ISBN	978 1 906578 11 4	PAGES	304pp
TITLE	Resource CD	PRICE	£39.99 + VAT
ISBN	978 1 906578 42 8	CONTENTS	Diagrams in jpeg format

Global Issues for CCEA A2 Level
Eileen Armstrong and Stephen Roulston

TITLE	Global Issues Book 1	PRICE	£12
ISBN	978 1 906578 57 2	PAGES	80pp
TITLE	Global Issues Book 2	PRICE	£12
ISBN	978 1 906578 58 9	PAGES	88pp